LEGACY

The Saga Begins

LEGACY

The Saga Begins

Nina and Mason,

Be Noble

[signature]

"Uncle MIP"

Written by Michael Pietrack
Illustrated by Catrina Odom

ISBN

979-8-9870996-2-9 (Hardcover)
979-8-9870996-0-5 (Paperback)
979-8-9870996-1-2 (Ebook)
979-8-9870996-3-6 (Audiobook)

I dedicate this book to my dad, David Pietrack,
the greatest storyteller on the earth,
who instilled in his sons to be noble.

At a time when American schools and cultural has become toxically cynical and political, Michael Pietrack takes readers, children and adults alike, back to a place of pure innocence and adventure. This journey is full of sincerity, imagination, and good morals. Pietrack's book utilizes beautiful traditional verse to elevate an otherwise charming tale to the level of great literary works where it leaves behind its own legacy.

—**Evan Mantyk**, Editor, Society of Classical Poets

Michael Pietrack's Legacy *is astounding, compelling, irresistible. Quite simply, it is the only book I have read, cover to cover, more than 20 times. I am convinced this will become a best seller and will be beloved by parents and children alike for generations to come.*

—**Theresa Dawn Sinclair**, author of
Children of Hamelin and *The Eternal Question*

Michael Pietrack's extraordinary work blends two genres, cross-pollinating them into a masterpiece that is sweet in every sense of the word. This amazing narrative of the imagination is what the world needs right now and will be read with joy for years afterward.

—**James Sale**, best-selling UK author
and feature writer for *The Epoch Times*

Legacy *is a gift. This thought-provoking tale helps us see that our choices in the face of fear define our legacy and inspire us to be noble. The principles in this book are applicable to life and business and gets my recommendation as a must-read.*

—**Mary B. Lucas**, author of *Lunchmeat* and
Life Lessons, international keynote speaker

Legacy is a unique work in a genre of its own. If one were to mix characters from Aesop with a plot by Tolkien, expressed through poetry that blends the accessible verve of Dr. Seuss with the descriptive richness of Keats, the result would be this epic fable of a bee that has no direct parallel in literary history. It is a masterpiece in the old sense of that term: something sophisticated that is capable of being appreciated by the average person—child and adult alike—and is a much-needed antidote to the moral vacuum of modern culture.

—**Andrew Benson Brown**, author of
Legends of Liberty, journalist, and editor

The imagery of this story is so clear that it feels like you are watching a movie. In fact, I can't wait for this book to be made into an animated motion picture. It will be a hit!

—**Danny Cahill**, author of *Aging Disgracefully*

Legacy shines, an instant classic that will go down in literary history.

—**Susan Jarvis Bryant**, poet and author

CONTENTS

ACKNOWLEDGMENTS

"And Abel's wise advisors beamed with pride,
who, with the parts they played, were satisfied."

Though writing is an activity done alone, getting a book to the market is not at all a solo mission. Simply acknowledging the profound help and kindness I received does not begin to express my gratitude to the many who helped *Legacy* find its way into your hands. Thank you to the vendors (especially Audivita and LaunchMyBook), and all our social media followers—Abel's legacy is now part of your own.

First and foremost, I thank my God, Jehovah. All praise goes to Him, the source of all wisdom and the giver of gifts and talents.

Secondly, I would like to thank my lovely wife, who allowed me to spend so much time to develop this story. I love you, Jamie, and I hope this makes you proud. Thank you for letting me be me.

Dad, you've always been my biggest fan in all of life's endeavors, but sharing the writing process with you has made this adventure all the sweeter. The little bee you used to tell us about as kids brought us even closer together as adults. In the end, this book is your legacy.

Catrina Odom, you took my ideas and put bones and sinew and flesh around them and brought them to life. The illustrations are world class. For both of us this has been *"quite an undertaking for one's debut."*

Dawn Sinclair, Legacy's first non-family fan and advocate, your reaction when you read the first draft, your encouragement and praise, was a gentle voice in a dark wilderness. Thank you Mama Dawn.

Andrew Benson Brown, I handed you a tangled meter mess and you taught me how to untie the knots. Thank you for coaching me and allowing me to utilize you as a sounding board so often. Along the way, I found a friend who inspires me to be a better writer.

James Sale, you brought an unknown, unproven, and unpolished poet in from the cold and welcomed him into your warm den. And in doing so, I met your talented son, Joseph Sale, who made me feel like kin. Thank you Lundy and Landry.

Holly Jacobson, you went from a super fan to my right hand assistant and became like family in the process. Whenever I feel down or discouraged, a call with Holly always lifts my spirits. Thank you for that.

The entire Pietrack Family Circus, thank you for your involvement large and small. Thank you for the encouragement and support and being my army of advocates.

My congregations in Colorado and Georgia, thank you for going on this journey with me and helping me make sure the story stayed wholesome. Thank you also for the wise reminders about humility and to keep squarely in focus the One who really deserves to be exalted.

Lastly, to my precious daughters, I love you with a depth I didn't know existed. Remember that what you choose to do in the snarling face of fear is what will write your legacy. Whenever you are in doubt and not sure what to do, be noble. Please, in this ignoble world, be noble. And please help Abel's words come true:

"I hope this expedition in the Wood
becomes a story that one day I could
share with my children, and then they with theirs,
who'll treasure it and prove they're worthy heirs.
Perhaps, they'll take great care to know it well;
their family saga that they're proud to tell."

FOREWORD

Legacy is the new narrative poem and imaginative fable from Michael Pietrack. It is an important work for our age and time. First, as narrative it is a gripping read of heroism, triumph over adversity, and of the confrontation with evil. As fable it joins the exalted ranks of the classics. The most famous fable of the classic world is, of course, Aesop's Fables; and the most famous of the twentieth-century is almost certainly George Orwell's Animal Farm. It is worth mentioning this last example especially because it is a wonderful expose of the political and philosophical nonsense that we call Communism. In other words, whilst fables may seem to be cute stories about various animals interacting, they at the same time can convey some of the profoundest insights into human nature and current realities.

So it is with Michael Pietrack's *Legacy:* perhaps the most important fable of the twenty-first century so far. The beauty of it too is that you can read it to your children and they will love it as well. It is simple to follow, yet has profound depth. And, as Andrew Benson Brown, the Missouri poet and critic, commented a while back: this poem is "a much-needed antidote to the moral vacuum of modern culture."

Written in charming, but not mechanical, verse, *Legacy* tells the story of the young Abelbee—a bee—on a quest to save his hive and queen. It is a classic odyssey story: the inexperienced and untested youngster who through the quest has to mature, realize his full powers, overcome obstacles and evil, and eventually become the hero he truly is—and save the hive! In short, the journey of Abelbee is every man and woman's journey if they are to live a full and satisfying life. Furthermore, as should be obvious: in order to overcome these terrors and obstacles on the journey, one must begin by overcoming them in oneself. Fear is the greatest enemy to all real achievement, and it begins within.

There are many, many moral lessons within the poem—but it is not 'preachy'. It is fast moving and the vivid imagery makes it feel as if one is—to use Danny Cahill's expression—"watching a movie." But for me I especially love the philosophical underpinning of the poem which explores perhaps the greatest philosophical dilemma of our age: I mean the question of free will. We live in a time where more and more people are self-designating as 'victims'—they did what they did or are what they are because they were determined that way; they had no choice. Against this pernicious helplessness and 'excusitis' stands Abelbee and his many supporters who—in exercising their wills, freely—take responsibility for all their actions and their consequences. That of course is exactly what all true heroes do: they refuse to be victims of circumstance and they define themselves by their actions.

Animal Farm is a very great fable, but it is a very bleak one: determinism rules and wins, and the story ends on a very horrific note that is characteristic of the twentieth century, the century of Hitler and Stalin. Michael Pietrack's *Legacy* ends very differently and I deeply hope that this is a portent of how the twenty-first century will go: not brought down by all the defeatists proclaiming that there is no free will, but elevated by all the heroes like Abelbee who insist on being heroes and through their decisions saving civilization, our hive.

It is because of these considerations, I think, that Evan Mantyk, the Editor of The Society of Classical Poets, wrote of *Legacy* that the "book utilizes beautiful traditional verse to elevate an otherwise charming tale to the level of great literary works where it leaves behind its own legacy." This seems to me to be profoundly true—as you will discover when you start reading this classic work! Dip in now—you won't be able to put it down.

James Sale
October, 2022

For behind the scenes extras, scan the QR codes with the camera on your smartphone.

AUTHOR'S NOTE

Many believe to destiny we're bound...
that laureled heroes and the queens we've crowned
are guided passengers on fortune's force
that moves along a predetermined course.

But if we're subject to what's meant-to-be,
we carry no responsibility.
And if no conscious choice was made or had,
then why reward the good or punish bad?

Yet there's another group who would contend
there is no master script that has been penned.
In every instant, history is written
with twisting plots inscribed by each decision.

Without a puppeteer, there are no strings,
which comes with freedom to decide all things.
And this endowment is a gift to use
that some will cherish—others will abuse.

So, which do you believe to be the case?
Are heroes mere selections by the fates?
Or do they earn each honored accolade
when fears are faced and valiant choices made?

Well, as you ponder that, please let me share
a story long ago placed in my care.
I'm curious to learn—what will you see?
Free will at work or fate's direct decree?

INTRODUCTION

"Please, Auntie, Auntie, read us Abelbee,"
the children asked. She reached for *Legacy*
and slid the book from its positioned place.
Collapsing volumes leaned to fill its space.

She sat and smiled at the familiar book;
its medal mirrored her nostalgic look.
She rubbed her thumb across the golden plaque,
and she prepared her heart for going back.

The children, three in all, were now abed
in silent waiting, and this is what she said:

I shall impart this story, kept in truth,
preserved and locked in safety since my youth.
My dearest father told it to me first
and often he'd retell it, verse-by-verse.

I promised him I'd keep it in beelore,
a history retold forevermore,
a fable for each future generation,
a rich anthology for all beenation.

This vital piece of history is yours
to treasure and ensure that it endures,
so teach your children as they're off to sleep,
for this is their inheritance to keep.

For behind the scenes extras, scan the QR codes with the camera on your smartphone.

CHAPTER 1

To see the illustrations in color, please visit www.TheLegacySaga.com.

PRIMDALE HIVE

Imagine flowered fields abloom in May,
as lazy breezes give tall grasses sway
and stir the zesty scents of Spring aloft,
which tease the bees who chase each floral waft.

Northerly, the Jubilee Meadow spread
up to a barn with walls of rusty red,
and in the morning shade of an oak tree,
the shadowed walls became deep burgundy.

The White Oak Tree wore weather-beaten bark,
where wrinkled scars of age had left their mark.
There, sheltered in her canopy of leaves,
was Primdale Hive that hung on branching eaves.

The charming hive had known an age of peace;
its bees enjoyed prosperity's increase.
The citizens were flourishing and free.
All thrived under their Queen, named Cimberlee.

Their domes and towers showed a wealth untold,
where Masonbees could build with bricks of gold.
They built a wall and gate of strength and sheen
around a palace to protect their Queen.

In solitude the stately White Oak stood
just off the Eastern edge of the Great Wood,
which was a forest vast and infamous—
a timberland, a darkened wilderness.

And running up the middle like a spine
stood tall imposing mountains in a line.
The Hog's Back was a fine and fitting name
to call a row of peaks, a mountain chain.

Some also called the Wood the Mayfair's Bell,
where many creatures teemed and thrived as well.
The Wood, though, was no place for meadow-bees,
and few had dared the darkness of the trees.

It housed more hazards than a bee could know.
Yet soon, you'll see, one will be asked to go.

SPECULATING WHISPERS

In Primdale Hive, there was a swirl of rumors,
where speculating whispers grew to murmurs.
An illness had impaired the Queen, they claimed.
(The sickness or the cause was never named.)

To cease conjecture and all false conclusions,
to dampen those developing delusions,
the Queen declared the bees to meet as one
at Center Hive, which soon was overrun.

The work of Masonbees and Workerbees
were halted in this time of great unease.
The Army Scouts and Soldiers each stood by
as both the Gatherers and Grangers ceased to fly.

Bees of all sorts, both common and with title,
made up a gathering that had no rival.
All shoulder-to-shoulder, hearing the decree
read by the Royal Crier, Bowmanbee.

RUNNING RAMBLINGS

The wood of Bowman's gavel banged three times,
resounding through the hollow hive's confines.
The hum of each continued conversation
kept Bowman from beginning his oration.

This warranted three more emphatic clacks,
which stopped all running ramblings in their tracks.
Then Bowman cleared his throat and showed the scroll
secured with seal and tied in tightened roll.

"Observe the scroll and that it is still bound.
As Royal Crier, loyal to the crown,
in sight I break the seal of Cimberlee
to read to you our regal Queen's decree:

"'My precious ones, the ones who call me Queen,
your voices have been heard, your glances seen.
You risk so much to aid the good of all;
I cherish each of you, the great and small.

"'Forgive my not addressing you in person;
I feared that my condition might soon worsen.
The rumors are correct—the danger's dire.
Without a cure, my heart will soon expire!'"

A low collective gasp came from the crowd
and then their chatter grew, increasing loud.
Bowman raised his arms to hush them down,
as he'd been given power from the crown.

"'Please hear your humble Queen's most heartfelt plea:
since Vallenbee will know my remedy,
one bee must travel deep within the Wood
to Vallenbee's Place that's found in Hannahgoode.

"'Only the fastest in the hive must go!
The only way, with certainty, we'll know
who is the proper bee to take this case
is for all Primdale Hive to hold a race!'"

Then Bowman paused to let the bees react—
the froth when fear and fervor interact.
As foaming bubbles poured over the mass,
the Crier stalled so thoughts could pop and pass:

"'Each family line will enter in one bee
at mid-day-next beneath the White Oak Tree.
This time tomorrow, all of us will know
who from among us will deserve to go.'

"And so prepare your hearts for what awaits
upon the trying trail to Vallenbee's Place.'
The clear insignia of Cimberlee
accompanies, *'Be noble, Primdale bees.'"*

THE HOME OF BALDWINBEE

In time, the bees at Center Hive dispersed
and plans were shared as family groups conversed...

This family saga, known as Legacy,
begins within the home of Baldwinbee.
He was a Mason known for muscle's might;
his look could level you with piercing sight.

Dear Gwendolee was Baldwin's lovely bride;
her outward beauty matched the belle inside.
Love radiated from her giving heart,
with depths of empathy no line could chart.

Their offspring was a son named Abelbee,
about full grown, with spry vitality.
But Gwen protected him, for he was born
with double wings; she feared the slings of scorn.

Back in that time, all bees throughout the Bell
had donned two wings aback and wore them well.
His four were rare in this part of the earth.
As far as Gwen knew, Abel was the first.

So, Gwen would try to hide his wings—she knew
that other youths would jeer as young ones do,
but what would keep her mind awake at night
is what great task his wings could yet invite.

And yes, he was the target of unkind bees,
who emptied quivers of quips that aimed to tease.
Their trusty arrow was to leave him out,
so Abel wore the wounds that caused self-doubt.

DISCUSSED AND DECIDED

In light of the day's news and its events,
young Abelbee was filled with true suspense,
but Baldwin's deepened voice was a percussion
against the walls that muffled a discussion.

So Abel didn't know what was in store
when he went walking through their chamber door.
His mother's sobbing eyes could not be stopped,
not even by her swabbing hands that mopped.

By nature, Abel grew in his concern
about what caused his mother's tears to churn.
But Baldwinbee declared with a father's firmness,
without a dance around the point or purpose.

"Son, it has been discussed and been decided,
based on the facts and feelings thus provided,
that I will fly tomorrow in the race.
And if I win, I'll shoulder what awaits."

Young Abelbee replied, "Just as expected,
but Mother, why are you so ill affected?
Does it not bring us honor and esteem
in putting forth our best to save the Queen?"

She said: "Sometimes, my tears have their own mind
and even my best fetters cannot bind
the fast unravel of a female's heart.
Oh, there's no stopping them when once they start.

"And even when I can't pinpoint the cause,
my impatient tears will seldom wait or pause.
My zeal is battling the fear within
that our brave Baldwinbee will likely win."

DESTINY'S INVITATION

As Abel tried to grasp what she had meant,
he noticed Baldwin's glance for Gwen's consent.
She nodded—Baldwinbee began to tell,
"I have already journeyed through the Bell.

"I'm not from Primdale Hive. I'm from up north—
a hive called Pollux at the Roaring Fork.
We call it Sweetbee Common, a prairie land,
a perfect meadow pollen-rich and grand."

With Baldwin's sigh, his memories were mist—
dissolved—this was no time to reminisce:
"I didn't follow Eagle River down
and didn't skirt the Wood or go around.

"I was the first to scale the Saddle Horn.
It was my destiny, why I was born.
Since I've traversed the Hog's Back once before,
I know all that the Wood will have in store."

Young Abel asked, "Why keep these things from me?"
Gwen said, "It wasn't time, my Honeybee;
it wasn't kept from you out of deceit."
Then Baldwin said, "Let's make the point complete.

"Compared to other bees within the hive,
I recognize that I'm most qualified.
So, I'll accept my destiny's invitation
and face the Wood without a hesitation."

In silence, Abel felt the story's weight
as Baldwinbee declared, "This is my fate.
This journey for the Queen was meant-to-be.
With clarity, I see it's meant for me."

With upward chin of honor on his face,
bold Baldwinbee was sure he'd ace the race.

HARBOR FOR A SECRET

Young Abelbee had laid awake that night;
his honest conscience launched a mighty fight.

To Abel, Baldwin was the bravest bee,
and knowing more of Baldwin's history,
the son believed his father would succeed—
that Baldwinbee would save the Queen in need.

But like his father, Abelbee was too
a harbor for a secret no one knew.
He never showed and no one ever asked,
but double wings made Abel twice as fast.

The chosen one would not be Primdale's bravest.
Not knowledge, strength, or height were any basis.
Pure speed alone would put one in position
to have success on this most crucial mission.

Torment would live with Abel all his days,
if deep within that wild wooded maze
his father was to find a bitter bend—
a dark concluding fall that meant his end.

The needed antidote would not arrive,
thus compromising Queen and bees and hive.
The mounting bloodguilt now that Abel faced
was sour in his mouth like nausea's taste.

If Abel were the family's chosen one,
the hive's great race could easily be won,
but the ensuing journey he would meet
was like a race that he could not complete.

GOLDIE

When Abel's mind would struggle to no end,
he'd seek the council of his only friend.
Sweet Goldenlee, as she was aptly called,
was granted access in what he had walled.

The day arrived, the morning of the race;
the two young bees met at their usual place.
As Abel poured out his conflicted heart,
sweet Goldie pulled the tangled tale apart.

She heard his case but Goldie was divided
on what advice to give, still undecided.
Restating: "You feel like you'll win the race,
but ill-equipped for what you'd have to face.

"Your father's both experienced and brave,
but if this journey leads him to his grave,
you'll be forever stung with guilt's remorse
that your own fear had put him on this course."

Then Goldie brought a new thought into light
that had evaded him the previous night:
"For if you let your father win and go,
his bravery the bees will always know.

"But think, what if your father comes up short
and gets portrayed as quite a different sort?
Forever branded 'failure' he'd be known,
if you deny the fate that is your own."

Uncoiled words had whipped him in the heart
and overwhelming thoughts made him depart.
But she could only watch him fly away,
not knowing what he'd do later that day.

She wrung her hands and wondered if her speech
had been an errant breaching overreach.
Each side is all she wanted him to see.
In whispered breath, "Be noble, Abelbee."

I see the heaviness upon your eyes—
The hour's late, it comes at no surprise.
So let your yawning mouth and eyes give way
and we'll continue on another day.

Let's dream what Abelbee decides to do.
What choice would you make were it up to you?
One's character is shown when one must choose
from situations that appear lose-lose.

So, close your weary veils and soon you'll see
the qualities we'll find in Abelbee.

For behind the scenes extras, scan the QR codes with the camera on your smartphone.

CHAPTER 2

To see the illustrations in color, please visit www.TheLegacySaga.com.

Within your bag of memories, retrieve
the words that spurred our Abelbee to leave.
He fled alarmed but could not fly away
from the decision he must make that day.

But sadly, Abel did not yet believe
for self-destructive whispers can deceive
and they grow louder as they are avowed.
They'll keep one's greatness quiet, if allowed.

Will Abel's skills be squandered by self-doubt?
Thus far, it seems his fears are winning out.
So come with me—before the race begins—
and we shall see just who it is that wins.

BEES FLY!

All Primdale Hive had gathered for the race.
The racers and their watchers set in place.
Within the cloudless blue, the sun was high,
as was excitement of those standing by.

Among the crowd, and torn by indecision,
was Abel tortured by his heart's division.
Though Gwendolee was standing by his side,
she didn't know his conflict fought inside.

The pride in Baldwin's chest was billowed sails
by wind from Gwen's applauding, cheering hails.
When Baldwin's wink to Abel didn't miss,
his smile back felt like betrayal's kiss.

The Queen attended looking sick and frail.
Her eyes were sinking coal's in a milkman's pail.
To speak would drain her needed energy,
so she deferred again to Bowmanbee:

"Our Queen has welcomed all to Primdale's Race.
She asks you show integrity and grace
by giving nothing but your very best.
For one of you, this moment starts your quest.

"From here, head southward, flying through the field.
Although the sprint is lengthy, do not yield.
Then take the turn around Forgotten Rock
and fly along the trail where grazers walk.

"The barn's big doors are closed, so go inside
through open windows on the southern side.
Weave through the stalls but watch for swishing tails,
then find the broken board between the bales...

"For that will be your exit from the stable.
The first returning here will prove he's able
to brave this quest and earn all Primdale's favor,
to be our winner and the one who'll save her.

"By powers granted me by Primdale Hive...
bees ready, one, two, three, bees fly!"

PRIMDALE'S RACE

The racing bees were off, a buzz, a swoosh.
Onlookers rooted, urging them to push.
While bee-contenders strained with all their might,
they jockeyed for an edge, however slight.

As Abelbee had watched the race begin,
adrenalin began to pump within.
Then like a revving throttle out of gear,
a rumble whir was drowning out his fear.

Before his thoughts could speak to stall or sway,
before his dread could hinder with dismay,
before his doubts deterred or could dissuade,
somewhere inside the bee a choice was made.

When he uncorked the torque in full ignition,
a rocket was released with full emission.
Right from the starting gate and through the meadow
the bee-crowd saw a streaking line of yellow.

He made up ground, a single darting dash,
and caught the racers in one flying flash.
Within congested traffic of the mass,
he slowed to switch his lane with spurts to pass.

Forgotten Rock was lying there alone,
yet it came fast just like the rock were thrown.
The hard right turn slid many off the course,
but Abel cornered tight and fought the force.

The straight away helped Abel pull ahead;
he looped inside the barn as Bowman said.
The window's opening was just a crack,
so Abel ducked, avoiding quite a smack!

The floating filament in shards of light
formed swirling wakes behind this jet in flight,
which stirred and made organic smells ascend.
The mix of hay and dung, a sour blend.

Within the stables, Abel weaved at will.
Unshackled now, he freed his hidden skill.
The horses there were busy eating straw
but seeing Abel stopped their grinding jaws.

Between the blocks of bristled hay in bales,
he whirled through broken boards and gnarled nails
as if escaping from a viper's bite
with its impaling fangs that plunge with might.

Ahead of Abel, Primdale's fastest bees
were racing towards the line at White Oak Tree.
But Abel gained and passed—the final stretch—
with only Baldwinbee now left to catch.

BEYOND THE FINISH LINE

Though both were racing for the finish fast,
the motion seemed to slow as Abel passed.
As Baldwin tried to process the events,
his Abel thought of choice's consequence.

He questioned, 'Could this destiny be mine?'
Then Abel looked beyond the finish line,
where on her throne sat watchful Cimberlee—
among them all the most important bee.

When Abel looked into her ailing eyes,
he grasped the race's scale and scope and size.
That if indeed the Queen were then to fall,
for Primdale Hive, it meant the end for all.

His heart, a hammered drum. The line approaching.
But then, without encouragement or coaching,
our Abel flicked his mighty wings once more.
He broke the line and then he heard a roar.

The baffled Baldwinbee, in second place,
was panting, reeling breathless from the race,
but more short-winded by this unseen shot,
a blindside blow that grew this father hot.

He grabbed his son and looked into his eyes,
expressing hurt, confusion, and surprise.
Baldwinbee rebuked, "What have you done?"
Just then a group of bees proclaimed, "You've won!"

On shoulders, Abelbee was lifted high
as bees began to pour back in the hive.
Baldwinbee was swallowed by the crowd;
his voice was lost amid those cheering loud.

The droves rejoiced in song, and as they streamed,
Abelbee was placed before the Queen.
Center Hive now amplified the hum
of Primdale's happy pandemonium.

THE CHOICE IS YOURS ALONE

The Queen found strength to stand; it hushed them down.
Her majesty was topped by shining crown:
"My victor, tell all Primdale Hive your name,
so we shall ever speak it with acclaim."

When Abel spoke, he heard his vocals shake;
he concentrated so they wouldn't break:
"My Queen, your Highness, I'm called Abelbee,
the son of Baldwinbee and Gwendolee."

A muffled mutter moved among the crowd,
so Bowman struck his gavel clear and loud.
The Queen was smiling wide at Abelbee
like seeing something only she could see.

But then she spoke to Abel pointedly,
no glaze upon the pill of poignancy:
"My health is failing, Abel, as you've heard,
but I am sure this illness can be cured.

"The only one who will know what to do
can only now be reached by one like you.
You've proven faster than the other bees,
which comes with true responsibilities.

"This journey deep into the vast unknown
is one you must confront all on your own.
So, if you feel this voyage is too great,
I'll understand and wipe it from your slate.

"But if you should accept and choose to go,
the name of Abelbee all hives will know
until the end of time, forever heard
and as familiar as a household word.

"Proud fathers naming sons will search but find
that only one great name will come to mind.
They'll want their sons and sons-of-sons to be
like you, and thus they'll name them Abelbee."

The Queenbee paused to catch her fading breath;
each word had come with taxes by the tenth.
She sat exhausted on her carried throne
and said to him, "The choice is yours alone."

A FATHER'S PLEA

Young Abel searched the crowd for Baldwin's eyes;
his validation was a treasured prize.
Approval was this son's necessity
but Abel's search did not find Baldwinbee.

His unresponsiveness concerned the crowd.
Despite the speed with which he was endowed,
perhaps he lacked the courage to accept.
Among the group a worried whisper swept.

Before he could give answer to his Queen,
a voice came from the crowd, someone unseen:
"STOP!"—an ardent voice with urgency.
Who was it drawing near? Baldwinbee.

He bowed, "My dearest Queen, both fair and kind,
I'm Baldwinbee and this young bee is mine.
Behold! From birth he's had four wings not two.
And we just witnessed what four wings can do.

"Though his surprising speed sets him apart,
he lacks the skills and fortitude of heart
to justify accepting this today.
I have a plan to share, if I so may."

The Queen allowed the floor to Baldwinbee;
she was aware of his brave history.
"My Queen, I see the urgency is great,
and by the blink you're in a worsened state.

"But Abel's necessary preparation
is, rightly so, this father's obligation.
We cannot send him off on this crusade
so sure to fail with an unsharpened blade.

"Please grant my son the needed time, dear Queen,
for me to share and Abelbee to glean
the priceless knowledge needed for success.
Let's build a heart of courage in his chest.

"I'll train him for what wanders in the Wood
and what lies lurking, both those bad and good.
Together we'll establish the approach
and we'll discuss each inquiry he'll broach.

"But if we still conclude that he is lacking,
despite the training and his solid backing,
then I would beg to go in my son's place,
and for your Highness, take this trying case."

The bee-crowd hummed and buzzed with their opinion,
although the say was in the Queen's dominion.
The Queenbee spoke, "Our intrepid Baldwinbee,
with favor I have heard a father's plea.

"Not only are you Abel's minister,
but too the race's second finisher.
So I accept your plan with one condition,
and it should only strengthen our position."

THE CALL

The Queen looked out upon a sea of faces,
so many loyal bees in her good graces.
"Step forward, please, our General Rykerbee."
(He led the Army Swarm and infantry.)

Rykerbee reacted as commanded
and one-knee-knelt as Cimberlee expanded.
"Our General, I know your heart so well,
and that you've vowed to always hear the bell.

"Again, in faithfulness, please heed the call,
although I recognize the task is tall.
Instruct him for expected battles fought.
Yes, martial crafts of combat must be taught.

"But stinger's skill alone won't get him there,
for still much more is needed to prepare.
Along with Baldwinbee, please utilize
two other expert bees who will advise.

"Yes, please allot him time with Dallenbee,
who will, in darkness, teach him how to see—
to navigate the Wood's known darkest places,
and how he can survive where no light graces.

"It's all for naught without the route and way.
I choose that Oglebee will have the say,
for he's our hive's most knowledgeable source
to map out Abelbee's most grueling course.

"From there, skilled Baldwinbee will be his teacher,
apprising Abel of each likely creature
residing in the Wood, and if they meet,
should Abelbee advance or take retreat.

"With Abelbee's advisors by his side
to share their wisdom, each a loyal guide,
our Abelbee should have all that he needs.
Please, Rykerbee, ensure that he succeeds."

Firm Rykerbee agreed, his head gave bow.
With that, the Queen continued on, "Well now,
our victor, Abelbee, will you agree
to take on this responsibility?"

Though insecurity had dropped his head,
he lifted up his eyes to hers and said,
"Your Highness, I'm afraid, still I say yes;
for Queen and hive I'll give my very best!"

Her smile was hoisted high and held by hope,
although her sickness yanked down on the rope:
"Well then, please rise and let all Primdale see
our carrier of hope, our Abelbee."

And that's the truth about the Primdale Race,
how Abel won our hearts and won first place.
I bet you are a lot like Abelbee
with talents that the world must wait to see.

But do your fears and doubts now hold you back
as anxious inner voices launch attack?
The narratives you tell yourself come true,
so often your worst enemy... is you.

Just wave away those thoughts like pesky gnats.
The one who beats his fear? The one who acts.
Remember this about those who are brave:
they still go forward even when afraid.

Soon you will meet those other sagely bees,
who'll speak the words of wisdom Abel needs.
I'll tell you all that happens next, I vow—
yet on another night. Goodbye for now.

CHAPTER 3

To see the illustrations in color, please visit www.TheLegacySaga.com.

Bring back to mind our story's prior scene,
where Abel gave his answer to the Queen.
Although he's won the famous Primdale Race,
still Abel has a bigger test to face.

He'll take the risky road to Vallenbee
with hope to bring the Queen her remedy.
But will it be a potion, plant, or pill
that cures Queen Cimberlee, who's fallen ill?

What vital lessons will young Abel gain,
and what new skills will the protégé attain?
Let's listen in, though it be exposition,
for you will need it on this expedition.

CRACKED FOUNDATIONS

The Queen outstretched her arms so to present,
"Please hear me now, that these bees represent
the qualities that well-define us all,
and with these bees, we all succeed or fall.

"I ask that Primdale backs dear Abelbee;
give him support just as if he were me.
Applaud the heroes standing here before us."
The name of Abelbee, a chanted chorus.

The look in Baldwin's eyes when Abel's met
were rich with meaning Abel tried to vet.
The true travail that furrowed Baldwin's face
revealed his toil to put it all in place.

Divided, Baldwin had competing thoughts,
where riled rivals each were taking shots.
Parental pride poured from this father's heart,
but also, worry's weight would not depart.

The anger that his son had disobeyed
had cracked foundations his beliefs had laid,
that each one has a destiny to run
and that this must apply now to his son.

Baldwin dreaded Gwen's forlorn reaction
at this completely unforeseen transaction.
She first had feared a husband she might lose,
but now, her only son was in the noose.

His riven heart must come together now
to help his youthful son fulfill his vow.

VICTORY'S EMBRACE

Abel's eyes explored the audience
for Goldenlee, who gave him confidence.
As Abel looked around without a trace,
his friend moved in for victory's embrace.

Once Goldie spun his chest, she held him tight,
which hid her smitten cheeks were blushing bright.
As these companions broke from their caress,
sweet Goldie had important thoughts to stress.

She said to Abelbee, "I know for sure
that you'll reach Vallenbee and find the cure.
When you return, you'll earn the Hero's Hum!
Your honor-share will be the greatest sum!"

With joy and fear both pulling at her heart,
her grin gave courage, thus it did its part.
Then Abel was escorted by the Swarm
and swept away as in a windy storm.

NO ONE WINS A FIGHT

The soldiers led him to the Warrior's Ward
to learn to wield his stinger and a sword.
His fencing master, Rykerbee, knew war,
a champion of battles from beelore.

He said, "The Swarm upholds the code that states:
'A war is won when kindness kills the hate.'
The truth is, Abel, though we train to fight,
a bee should never be the first to strike.

"A single act of peace can turn a foe.
In war, there is no more effective blow
than changing hearts from enemy to friend.
If strike-for-strike, then war would never end.

"Yet with that said, you should learn how to fence;
if nothing else, I'll teach you self-defense.
But even if I taught you several stings,
still your most useful weapons are your wings.

"With knowledge of what's lurking in the Wood,
my strong advice to you is that you should
fly fast and far at every chance you can.
For one to stand and fight—a foolish plan.

"And that's the biggest lesson of the night—
remember Abel, no one wins a fight.
Yet still, at times, one's forced to make a stand,
to point their stinger or to ball their hand.

"Supposing you are cornered in a place
confronted by opponents face-to-face,
if battle comes no matter what you do,
well then, make them regret a fight with you."

NEVER LET THAT SPILL

Into the night, he trained with Rykerbee,
who taught with patience, poise, and quality.
The discipline of Ryker's proven way—
a lighted path from which he'd dare not stray.

Because of Abel's heavy-labored breath,
his teacher thought it best to give him rest.
And Ryker stated, "You have done quite well.
Your quick improvements have been plain to tell.

A WAR IS WON
WHEN KINDNESS
KILLS THE HATE.

"May each technique now serve you faithfully,
deploying strategies most gracefully.
The wasps especially are ones to fear;
reports bring news that they've been drawing near.

"Avoid and flee from them at any cost.
And, even if it means your life is lost,
do not let them find out the Queen is ill,
so lock your lips and never let that spill."

Detecting depth in Rykerbee's request,
with care, he placed the words within his breast.
Then Abel's begging question sought relief:
"Is all of this just leading us to grief?
What if the answers sought from Vallenbee
surpass the wise one's capability?"

"Your trusted Queen would not ask you to go,
if she lacked certainty that he would know.
And I'm convinced that Vallen will provide
the cure... for he's uniquely qualified."

ONE ADVENTURE LEFT

We next find Abel high within the hive
with Oglebee, the eldest bee alive.
His office window opened to the East.
To see the path made Abel's fear increase.

"I wish that I could go along with you,
but true, those days have passed as all things do.
Although within my mind I am still young,
this cracked decrepit shell sure spoils the fun.

"In youth, each day is ripe and for the taking,
but when you're old, each day is withered waiting.
It seems as soon as life's pursuits begin,
they roll away like tumbleweeds in wind.

"I have but one adventure left, my boy,
although prepared, that journey I avoid—
a Wood so dark, no voyagers return.
What lies beyond, no witness can confirm.

"The Wood ahead of you is not like that.
A number who have entered in came back,
and I am one who lived to tell the tale.
I've toed the trail, recalling each detail.

THE PATH

"The path I'll show you, I took years ago.
I had a special gift-in-hand to show—
a little something made for Vallenbee.
The trip is long and no part's danger free."

He turned and opened up his wrinkled hand
and his left palm became that wooded land.
Then with his right-hand finger, like a quill,
he charted Abel's course with seasoned skill.

"A natural seam exists where Timber Top
begins and where the Ponderosas stop.
You'll know the trees are Ponderosa Pine
by sharpened leaves, a needle thin design.

"Stay on the side where leaves are flat and wide
for they provide a better place to hide,
but note that birds use them for hiding too.
Each tree has eyes and they'll be stalking you."

That bitter thought had sickened Abel's heart.
He winced and pursed like tasting something tart.
"You can be focused on your goal, and yet
acknowledge danger and its constant threat.

"So always keep in view the mountain chain
that parts the Wood just like a horse's mane.
Your target is the mountain Shadow Black,
the tallest peak among the Hog's Back.

"And be forewarned about the Darrington Straits,
where Bladenbee and other beewolves wait.
Go South, around the Strait, if you are wise;
to go right through would mean your sure demise.

"Beyond the Strait, toward the peaks, you'll find
the most exquisite place known to beekind.
The fields of Leahlora—they are true!
Her buds will beckon and replenish you.

"You'll see both hummingbirds and butterflies
ballet about beneath her perfect skies.
Although your heart will beg with pleasing song,
you should not linger there or loiter long.

"Depart and cross the winds atop the stream
and find the cave, whose mouth's a silent scream.
Within, a tunnel bores completely through."
With each description, Abel's worry grew.

"Wa-Wait... go through a cave? What do you mean?
Is there no other way to save the Queen?
For you describe a dingy habitat
that likely teems with vicious vile bats!"

"It homes more bats than any bee could count
and reaching it by dusk is paramount."
—"Dear Oglebee, is there no other way
than sending in the open mouth... the prey?

"I can't go in a lightless bat-filled cave!"
—"But three days of your journey will be saved.
For every hour spent incurs a cost;
there's no redeeming time when once it's lost.

"I have a plan so that you'll never face
a loathsome bat within that cavernous place.
At twilight, they go out to hunt their prey
and that's when you go in, when they're away.

"The cold vacated cave, though it be black,
will offer safety till the bats come back.
The cave is not a shelter, so beware,
and when the bats return, do not be there!"

All wound with worry, spun in stirred suspense,
young Abel's clasping hands were tight and tense.
"Beyond the cave, you'll find Linosa's ponds,
with her most mesmerizing Windy Blondes.

"Then find the trail amid the silver trees,
for it will take you straight to Vallenbee's—
a tree that looks like two but grows as one
and dressed in vines that twine and overrun.

"Beneath the southern-facing branch, in shade,
will be a hollow a woodpecker made.
That's Vallenbee's Place, protected out of sight,
and oh, I pray that you'll reach it alright."

GOOD AND BAD AND THE DIVINE

Then Abel said "I'm feeling most unfit;
I seek a target that I'll never hit.
Fate's boney finger that now points at me
selected by mistake the wrong bee!"

Gray Ogle smiled, "It's odd how lives play out,
I've often wondered if we choose our route,
or if one's life is driven all by fate.
Ah well, I guess that is the great debate.

"The forces seen within this life of mine
are three: there's good and bad and the divine.
The force of badness seeks to dominate
for pride and greed, for power, lust, and hate.

"The force of goodness always aims for peace
and hopes that love and selflessness increase.
These forces tug at every living thing,
and all must choose which force they crown as king.

"My Abelbee, if good is your main trait,
then every path is straight—no test too great.
And if you place your trust in the divine,
then everything just seems to work out fine."

These reassuring words gave Abel hope,
yet Ogle saw how doubt resumed to grope,
so Ogle said, "This is a trusted track—
but Vallen will decide the best route back."

BLIND

Next, Abel met outside with Dallenbee,
a Duke awarded full nobility
for acrobatic feats and daring stunts
that chilled and thrilled the audience at once.

"See Abel, flying blind is my forte;
I always fly at night as some might say.
I'm nearly blind and been that way since birth.
I'll share what I have learned, for what it's worth."

"Blind since birth? I would have never guessed;
among the royal court, you fly the best."
—"They said I'd never be an acrobat.
Well, I just simply disagreed with that.

"Everyone is born with handicaps,
but we control if they will hold us back.
The only disabilities we've got
are limits we've created or been taught."

"It's such an honor to meet you, Dallenbee.
You're imitated in the Jubilee."
—"But now the children will pretend they're you:
'Abel... the fastest bee who ever flew!'"

Though flattered much, a worried heart remained.
To face the pitch-black cave, he wasn't trained.
"What should I do when lost in some dark place?
How can I use my speed in such a case?"

"The air gets warm when something is close by;
the air is cooler when you're clear to fly.
With careful practice, you will get it right,
so you don't get it wrong on that dark night!

"Your two antennae were designed so well;
they're capable to see and feel and smell.
Their rattle-shake won't lead you off astray,
so trust in them to find and light your way."

As Dallen taught, young Abel listened well.
His waves of fear were calm without a swell,
but then a whopping wave returned to shore:
"There's something else that haunts me even more.

"It may not be a fearful thing to you,
but faced with this, I must know what to do.
Instructions, word-for-word, I aim to keep—
without a hive at night, where should I sleep?"

"I don't make light in that you fear the dark.
For though your eyes won't see, your ears will hark
upon so many unfamiliar sounds
and, though you'll look for them, they won't be found.

"But never has a noise impressed a mark.
Ignore them like you would a rude remark.
I've found that noisy ones are most afraid,
they hope to scare you off by noises made.

"So find a bud that opens up by day,
and like an undiscovered stowaway,
the closing flower will house you for the night.
You'll be protected, warm, and out of sight.

"The flower closes as the darkness falls,
and when it does, don't be outside its walls.
I beg you Abel, don't make that mistake
for when the flower closes, it's too late."

The simple brilliance gave vitality.
What's wisdom without practicality?
And at the end, as they prepared to part,
his mentor had one thing left to impart:

"At times, you cannot trust what you perceive.
Though you have sight, beware how it deceives.
In fact, our very eyes can make us blind—
a frightful face can hide a heart that's kind."

Arriving home, the hour dimmed the stage,
where, pacing like a lion in a cage,
his eager father sought a full debrief.
Instead, he let his son get needed sleep.

Since Abel's set to rest, then so shall we.
It seems your sleepy lids don't disagree.
Absorb the given counsel while you sleep,
forever your possession now to keep.

We learned that sight's a gift beyond compare,
yet our own vision can become impaired.
We learned that goodness is a force within,
but the opposing force will try to win.

The battle must be won inside ourselves
for we will act as how our heart compels.
Dwell on this final thought, for it is late,
that only loving kindness conquers hate.

CHAPTER 4

To see the illustrations in color, please visit www.TheLegacySaga.com.

Recall what Abelbee was taught and told.
Are they now your own priceless jewels to hold?
Brave Ryker said that no one wins a fight
and Dallen warned about deceiving sight.

Remember Abel's path on Ogle's palm
where, with his finger, Abel's map was drawn?
Next, Baldwinbee's advice is on the docket
with secret gems for Abelbee to pocket.

OUT THERE

When Abelbee awoke, his dad was waiting,
yet deep in thought on plans and concentrating.
Then Baldwin said, "Please come outside with me."
He took his son out to the Jubilee.

The meadow, damp with dew, was appetizing;
each smell and color tempted—tantalizing.
They ate of nectar rich and pollen bold
upon a patch of pristine marigold.

Once they had eaten, feeling quite replete,
they rested on some lupines for a seat.
"That's Ponderosa, where you'll enter in."
(And Baldwin pointed East to center-in.)

"And when that threshold's broken, you will find
a world that's unforgiving and unkind—
for life within the Wood is unlike here.
Out there, my son, there's danger always near.

"Look out for bellbirds, spiders, frogs, and bats.
And don't consort with mosquitoes, flies, or gnats.
Avoid beewolves who hide themselves in ash.
And flee from dragonflies and wasps that gnash!

"Please listen closely—wasps are not like bees.
They lack the longing in their hearts for peace.
We only strike attack if we're provoked;
our fires only singe when they are stoked.

"But to a wasp, inflicting pain is sport,
not simply some assault's required retort.
As if it's honey, evil is produced,
and they're creative how the pain's induced.

"Their eyes are filled with hate, which fuels their lance.
And they are ever looking for a chance
to overpower bees and make them slaves.
No pity shown to those they send to graves."

BOUND IN CHAINS

Though Abel's larynx fought to stay afloat,
he tugged a swallow down his tightened throat
and said, "Oh Father, please, what have I done?
I may be fast but look! I'm not the one.

"It's right that you should go instead of me...
You're always brave! You go to Vallenbee!
—"Who won the race? Was it me or you?
I cannot trade your four in for my two!?"

He wondered why his father didn't seize
the offer that he could have grabbed with ease.
Yes, Abel pondered why he took that stance—
to not reclaim the quest. He had the chance.

Those thoughts were silenced by an interruption
as Baldwin longed to give him this instruction:
"My son, you have to look at fear two ways,
and this is true for all your living days.

"The first—remember fear's a lifeless thing.
Alone it has no wing; it has no sting.
Some give it life and cede controlling reins.
Then fear's a lord who keeps one bound in chains.

"For instance, when I flew the Horseshoe Pass,
I weaved around the stocks of lanky grass.
In suffocating fear, I drowned in dread
because the pass had led to Colony Red.

"Oh Abel, I was panicked to the core—
I found myself alone at the wasp's front door!
But chaffs of grasses in the open field
had helped your father hide and stay concealed."

Awash with youthful curiosity,
true interest brimmed and spilled from Abelbee,
for though these monsters made all bees afraid,
the topic thrilled while mounting tension weighed.

"I looked at Rory-Vespa."—"Their mighty king?"—
"Yes son, and feared his potent, lethal sting!
He was from me to you but didn't see,
obscured by grass, this hidden frightened bee.

"The ring of my antennae buzzed so loud,
I feared it was detected by the crowd.
I posed for combat with my stinger flared
and could have caught the king most unprepared.

"I could have slashed red Rory-Vespa through,
thus paying back this evil his fair due,
but fear kept me from trusting my impulse.
Because, what if my plan had proven false?

"What if my ever-daring lunging lance
had only nicked him with harmless glance?
No matter if my strike was off or true,
surrounding scouts would have struck me through.

"I doubted in myself; fear made me pause.
Now biting guilt—regret—oh, how it gnaws.
But if again I meet that wicked foe,
my fear won't bind me—I would strike a blow.

"I fled with urgency and headed south
and found the windy shores at Bread Creek's mouth.
I was so scared, I even dared to cross;
I found it safer than to face a wasp."

He saw his father in a different light,
to know that he gave way to feeling fright.
But Baldwinbee continued with his speech;
he had another lesson yet to teach.

A WILD HORSE

"Though fear's a figment, know that danger's real;
the brave use fear to make the danger kneel.
The second truth—your fear enhances skill,
but only when it's harnessed by your will:

"Imagine both a man and wild horse,
a clash of strategy and will and force.
The animal refuses to be ridden,
like being tamed and hacked was most forbidden.

"The horse then flares its nostrils, whines its neighs,
and tries intimidating kick displays.
But undeterred he ropes the fierce equine
and when he mounts the stud, their strengths entwine.

"The punching force that was at first opposing,
that mountain made of muscle first imposing,
was now controlled by reigns held in his hands,
so that the wrangled stallion heeds commands.

"Your fear can prove to be an enemy,
but if corralled, a spurring energy.
To master fear with bridle, bit, and bar,
is how the gallant gallop fast and far."

A LEGACY

Upon the petals, Abelbee explained
what all his mentors taught and he had gained.
But still he sought more wisdom from his father,
as seeking pages from his favorite author.

Next Baldwin felt the thing that was still lacking
was not defensive skills for strikes attacking,
no other markers that he must recall,
no added warnings now would help at all.

There was one final thing that was remaining,
which would complete his son's most needed training.
Young Abelbee now had to visualize
not vicious perils, but the victor's prize.

To give his son the gift of confidence,
now more important than imparting competence.
No metal's worth the value of good advice,
yet mettle ups its value more than twice.

Baldwin did not meander to the point—
a prophesy that did not disappoint:
"My son, the dream of every single bee
is that their life will leave some memory,
a tiny mark that says that they were here.
But time erodes and most names disappear.

"Yet, when you make it back and save the Queen,
your branded mark will be forever seen—
a legacy to be revered and shared,
to which no one's could bear to be compared."

This arrow hit its mark in Abel's soul,
and he could finally see this peerless goal:
"I hope this expedition in the Wood
becomes a story that one day I could
share with my children, and then they with theirs,
who'll treasure it and prove they're worthy heirs.
Perhaps, they'll take great care to know it well;
their family saga that they're proud to tell."

MY DESTINY

His son's true confidence was wealth amassed,
but Baldwin knew this currency goes fast,
so prudently he stocked the storehouse plumb
with words of merit added to the sum.

"I thought for sure this journey was my fate.
I'd bring the Queen back to a healthy state.
With Vallenbee, we'd solve the mystery—
a closing chapter to my history.

"But now, as I've seen these events unfold,
I see an opening chapter yet untold.
But this most epic tale is yours, not mine,
and in that way our destinies align.

"I see and now embrace my destiny:
I get to be the dad of Abelbee."
And with those words, he could have taken on
a horde of wasps, yes, their entire throng!

Baldwinbee was not at all the type
to love with words or praise his every stripe,
so having full support from Baldwinbee
was greater than an army's weaponry.

PREPARED

Though Abelbee was filled with inspiration,
a thought imbued a tinge of trepidation
and so he asked, "Am I prepared to go?"
His father didn't grant concern to show.

"There are so many things in life you'll face
that feel like twists before there's time to brace.
When I was told that I would have a son,
I knew the needed skills... and I had none!

"Though with a heart determined to succeed,
I found unknown and dormant skills were freed.
And as I look upon my son today,
it would appear I somehow knew the way...

"So like when one first faces parenthood,
no one is ever fit to face the Wood."
The illustration had a small affect
upon the youth, so Baldwin went direct:

"I see you're scared but know I would be too.
In fact, all bees would feel just like you do.
But courage in the face of fear, my son,
is not the path embarked by everyone.

"Without fear, then courage can't exist;
you triumph only when a force resists.
A stand of courage takes a moment. However,
a moment of courage, my son, will stand forever."

COME BACK TO ME

The final night before his odyssey,
he spent some needed time with Gwendolee.
His caring mother, eager now to speak,
but first, a tender kiss upon his cheek.

"My Honeybee, to live to serve the Queen
is the highest honor known to any bee.
And though in principle I'm in accord,
I am still struggling to get onboard.

"Because the thought of you alone out there,
so vulnerable, no margin room to err,
wells up the truest fear I've ever known.
You must forgive the tears my face has shown.

"And listen well and hear my desperate plea:
Succeed Abel! You come back to me!"

Her tears careened around her solemn smile,
as she enfolded arms around her child.
He sensed his mother's labor as she clutched
and Abel felt her tears as their cheeks touched.

ONE YOU FOR ME

The mother held and rocked her cradled son
and sang a soothing song she often sung:

"There's just one you for me,
for me, it's you.

There's just one me for you,
for you, it's me.

There's just one us to be,
that's you and me.

And when I'm not with you,
I'm just not me."

GUARANTEE

Then Gwen composed herself to say with care,
"My Honeybee, I'll be with you out there.
I have a promise, yes, a guarantee:
that every single time you think of me,
at that exact same moment, I'll be too,
with fondness, thinking loving thoughts of you.

"Please often think of me and you'll find strength.
Though I may seem so far, I'm at arm's length.
So reach, my love, yes always reach again;
my hand is reaching on the other end."

FAREWELL

The morning's chalk drew periwinkle skies
as Abel wrestled belly-butterflies,
but they refused to fly in V-formation.
He tried long breaths to calm the odd sensation.

Again, the bees convened at Center Hive
and cheers rang out to see their Queen arrive.
Her carried throne was gliding through the air;
six loyal subjects bared the weight with care.

The throne was lowered gently on its spot,
like placing a sleeping baby on its cot.
Our Abelbee was there among the crowd.
When Bowman called him to the throne, he bowed.

Their Queen sat hunched like wind had bent the reed.
The gavel dropped—Bowman began to read:
"Dear Abelbee, your flight will make beelore,
the theme of rhyming tales forevermore.

"And when we hear those stories told, we'll say
with pride that we were present on this day.
But now we will await with hearts that yearn
to hear of your successful, safe return.'

"Signed Cimberlee, her appended postscript reads:
'I bid farewell—Be noble, Abelbee.'"

The bee's kazooing buzz had filled the room,
and when it faded, Bowman could resume:
"The General requests that Baldwinbee
attend his escort to the Jubilee"

The Queenbee mustered strength to stand and speak
and, like a newborn doe, legs wobbled weak.
To Abelbee now standing at her throne,
she said, "Your eyes tell me that you have grown.

"When you meet Vallenbee, please let him know
that you were sent by Cimberlee—now go!"

And now it's time for us to go as well.
As did the Queen, I bid you my farewell.
The time we've spent has yielded quite a profit;
we leave with treasures in our purse and pocket.

Remember even Baldwinbee was scared
and for the Wood, no one could be prepared.
So, when your fear's a stallion grab the reins,
for mettle's worth more than what metal gains.

What dark foreboding wilderness ahead
now gives you pause with thoughts of doubtful dread?
Don't wait because those feelings never fade,
for bravery means doing it afraid.

Soon Abel's virgin voyage will commence
with many unforgettable events.
The stories yet to come are worth the wait
but now it's time for sleep, the hour's late.

CHAPTER 5

To see the illustrations in color, please visit www.TheLegacySaga.com.

Escorted by his father and Rykerbee,
young Abel flew outside to the White Oak Tree.
There Baldwin's hand shook Abel's—resolute—
as Ryker gave the Army Swarm salute.

From Ryker's fist that balled against his chest,
his arm and hand were opened from his breast
as if he gave his heart to Abelbee—
a gesture and an oath of loyalty.

Though Baldwinbee was silent, standing strong,
the father felt withholding words was wrong.
But Baldwin had so much to say that none
would come except the words: "Be noble, son."

The cherished lessons fresh in Abel's mind,
will all be needed, as you're sure to find.
Prepare yourself for many wild spins
as Abelbee's adventure now begins...

BATTLE-HARD PLATOON

When Abel reached the storied Meadow's Edge,
he thought how often Gwen would make him pledge
to never go to this forbidden place,
yet likely, it's the safest one he'd face.

Not once in his most far off fantasy
did Abel dream he'd have the chance to see
the gabled pines of Ponderosa's forest,
nor ever thought that he would be its tourist.

The trees were troops fatigued in army green,
upright, alert and still as figurines.
Saluting at attention, soldiers stood.
A battle-hard platoon nicknamed the Wood.

In looking up at them, his body arched.
It seemed at any minute they would march,
with booming booted beats all synchronized,
and he'd be trampled by their crushing strides.

THE BRINK

Abel turned and gazed from where he came,
but now his home no longer looked the same.

The once extraordinary mammoth Oak
had seemed more like a painter's thin brush stroke.
The big red barn was now a tiny dot—
a needless touch the artist near forgot.

In looking back, it caused him agony;
to circle back, a pull like gravity.
This was the brink—the line he dared not cross.
Now all those warnings must be tossed like dross.

Abel fought the urge and fierce unease
to face the lonely road into the trees...

THE STRANGER

His stinger tucked was like a frightened tail.
With his antennae perked, he edged the trail.
The leaves and fronds seemed useful for obscuring
himself from hunters finding him alluring.

But Abel's sly maneuvers were in vain;
the stranger's presence in the Wood was plain—
his stealthy steering, clumsy as a crash;
his blending in was more like color-clash.

Camouflaged among the leaves and baiting
was a bellbird, mossy-green and waiting.
The fumbling foreigner had botched his foray
into the Wood by stumbling to her doorway.

The idle bird was feeling like a thief;
the effortless meal caused happy disbelief.
She opened wide for this delivered gift
but she was left astonished when she whiffed!

So, in her quick attempt at blot the blunder
and to recover her most coveted plunder,
she zigged and zagged among the branch's leaves.
The hungry bird had matched him weave for weave.

Then Abel saw a nook within a tree
and swooped inside; the huntress didn't see.
The hole was small—his body squeezed to fit.
There Abel waited for the bird to quit.

He watched his chaser carry on her hunt
and knew she wasn't one he should confront.
In her dismay, the huntress flew away
to start a search for less resilient prey.

TURN AROUND

Though Abel felt secure inside that nook,
he moved out from the knot to have a look.
A voice then scared him back into the hole:
"Well, hello there. Out for a morning stroll?"

With his antennae straight and more aware,
he one-eye-peeked to find out who was there.
And he saw Sova, an ostentatious owl,
a self-distinguished Ponderosa fowl.

As Sova perched upon a lengthy bough,
his amber eyes, beneath a bushy brow,
were opened wide as was his puffy chest.
His tufts of horn-like feathers crowned his crest.

And nothing stirred the owl's pretentious soul
like casting himself to play the leading role.
No sport showcased his self-appointed station
quite like theatrical pontification.

"It's rare to see a bee outfly a bird.
It's actually preposterous, absurd!
I must have seen a dragonfly or locust."
He spun his neck, "C'mon, old bird, now focus!

"My mind must still be foggy from my nap.
How could a meadow-bee avoid that trap?
For never in my Ponderosa days,
has any bee maneuvered in those ways.

"Perhaps a wasp? But no, he's far too little!
Whatever you are, you're quite a vexing riddle."
The owl, fatigued from his deliberation,
soon lost all interest in the rumination:

"You there, the one who's hiding in the knot.
Do tell, ole boy, are you a bee or not?
Ha ha, to bee or not to bee. Quite right!
C'mon, now you can't stay in there all night."

Not sensing any ill intent was had,
young Abelbee stuck out his head.—"Good lad!
I see the head of a bee poking out
and bet the other half is bee, no doubt!

"So, satisfy my curiosity,
what business has you in the Wood, young bee?"
While still remaining guarded about this meeting,
our careful Abelbee explained, retreating.

"I'm on a quest that's only just begun."
At such a claim, the neck of Sova spun.
—"A quest? What sort of bee-quest could there be?
Pah! That sounds just like beeswax to me.

"Quite right! It's clearly a cockamamie thought.
So, have you reached your goal inside that knot?"
The owl enjoyed his sense of comedy
and snickered at his wit and oddity.

His quest, then Abel tried to dignify
by giving the condescending bird reply:
"They sent me on a journey to Vallenbee's Place."
—"Well, well, well, is that the case?

"Important business must be taking at hand,
but this bee-brained quest is not well-planned.
To send a youthful bee to Hannahgoode
is a death march into the Great Wood!

"A fool's errand is much more apropos.
You see, my lad, they were too scared to go.
'Let's send the naive numpty; he won't mind.'
And here you are, unarmed, on the front line.

"Trust me, meadow-bee, the outcome's grim
so go back home, the odds are far too slim.
Why try when failure is a certainty?
No shame in quitting this absurdity.

"If you have any common sense at all,
you'd turn around and fly and say with gall,
'Thank you but I decline your fine request.
Assign some other twit this worthless quest!'"

His cynicism was a foreign tongue;
his patronizing, smug speech stung.
Young Abel said, "In any honest eyes,
this quest is classed the highest honored prize."

"Ah, there it is, the innocence of youth,
that's not yet marred by the embittering truth.
What you've been taught to find commendable
was sold then bought by one expendable."

Though he knew Sova's words were false indeed,
some wielded words wound deep enough to bleed.
Although he tried to handle himself with poise,
his face revealed the sting of Sova's ploys.

SOVA THE GREAT

"Don't let this snarky owl cloud your skies
or tarnish any sheen upon your *prize*.
Perhaps, I'll kindly aid your bee-endeavor.
There's no one in the Wood that's half as clever.

"What could you have to give to Vallenbee?
What treasure would one send with this 'trustee'?
Or... Ah... perhaps with greatest urgency
you bear the news of grave emergency?..."

When Abel looked away in wise refrain,
then Sova knew there must be more to gain.
He said with pry and prod, "... Quite right, I see.
Do tell, ole boy, your secret's safe with me."

In silence, Abel reasoned how to dodge
the foul owl's inquiry barrage
and said, "All bees are faithfully discrete;
the secrets that we hold, we don't repeat.

"But you are most correct, I do need aid
for off my path, I fear I must have strayed.
That bellbird's chase has spun me all around,
my bearings lost in unfamiliar grounds."

"Though Ponderosa is my humble home,
there is no Mayfair branch I haven't known.
And I have even been to Vallenbee's Place.
It's just a shanty... rather shabby taste."

—"You know Vallenbee?"—"Of course I do!
This is Sova the Great you're speaking to!"
Then Abel saw the winning strategy
would be to douse the bird in flattery.

"You truly are the wise one of the Wood.
Your Eminence, I wonder if you could...
no... no... it's much too large a thing to ask,
and even for Sova the Great, too tough a task..."

Without suspicious thought to Abel's lure,
he took the bait but wasn't hooked for sure:
"This beeish bumble is starting to annoy.
Too tough a task? Pah! Out with it, boy!"

"Since Sova the Great *of course* knows well the way
and Vallenbee must have respects to pay,
perhaps, as my heroic escort,
you'd kindly carry me across the court...?"

"Pah! Your tiny mind has got you dizzy.
No, no, no, Sova's far too busy."
—"To find out why I'm seeking Vallenbee,
you'd have to choose to come along with me."

"Well, I surrender and am at your feet.
You've conquered me and my entire fleet.
Pah! You try to sly with my own tricks,
but this wise hound no longer chases sticks.

"My minor interest was a whim at best.
Now you've begun to bore me with this quest.
Plus, this nonsense is no fate of mine,
and bee-affairs are a waste of Sova's time."

Young Abel sighed defeated, disappointed
that hidden snares were easily avoided,
for Sova threw the hook by his rejections.
All Abel could gain now were some directions.

He looked and saw that only needle leaves
were found upon the tall surrounding trees.
"To Timber Top—can you please point the way?"
—"Pah! My lad, 'To Timber Top' you say?

"Your simple ask requires me no labor
for Timber Top is Sova's next-door neighbor!
Quite right, yes, fly that way and in no time
you'll reach the end of Ponderosa Pine.

"And there, my boy, the Timber Top awaits,
but do avoid the gray of Darrington Straits."
Then Sova spread his wings and took to flight
and mumbled to himself, "Yes, yes, quite right."

As Sova flies away, we should as well.
Where do we fly when under slumber's spell?
I hope you go to lands of dulcet dreams
that have no cynical Sovas or bellbird schemes.

A land that's free of hurtful mean remarks,
those condescending nipping bites and barks.
But Sova's antics showed that cynicism
is just a phony's forgery of wisdom.

Don't let a snide naysayer make you cry;
their speech dissuades when they're too scared to try.
Will Abel be discouraged and turn for home,
or will he brave the wooded vast unknown?

CHAPTER 6

To see the illustrations in color, please visit www.TheLegacySaga.com.

Recall the owl declined the invitation
to go along or give him transportation.
Though Sova's gone, his words would still harass
as Abel flew to Timber Top and fast.

Young Abelbee assumed all in the Wood
must be as harsh, concluding none were good.
But soon he'll find that theory incorrect.
Who will our Abelbee run into next?

THE DARRINGTON STRAITS

When Abel found the seam within the Wood,
it led to where the greatest trees once stood
before a fire disfigured trees to dust
and melt the seal of fate and one unjust.

The Darrington Straits, it's been referred to since.
The ash is guarded by the Beewolf Prince.
There, banished Bladen's tribe made homes in soot,
a hazardous place for those on wing or foot.

The wolves were exiled to the ashy gray
because they turnèd to live a monstrous way.
Instead of nectar, they began to crave
the taste of flesh and they became its slave.

These cannibals, with their unnatural thirst,
now live in isolation—most accursed.
Within their squalid homes among their waste,
they wait for flesh and blood. Oh, just a taste.

MOTHER'S HAND IN REACH

Through charred and absent forest, Abel saw
the rigid mountains Ogle tried to draw.
As Abel gaped across the wide expanse,
a tender voice awoke him from his trance.

"My dear, are you about to dare the Strait?
Don't go in there for hidden wolves await."
Then Abel turned and saw a deer and fawn.
"This is my son, Sinclair; I'm Mama Dawn."

The mother's caring eyes with lashes long
were just as soothing as his mother's song,
and in the deer's familiar gentle speech,
young Abel felt his mother's hand in reach.

He smiled and said, "My name is Abelbee."
Mama Dawn replied, "You worried me
because you looked like you were going in.
My dear, a grave mistake that would have been!"

OVERCONFIDENCE

Sinclair then said, "Well, I ain't scared of the Strait!"
He flexed his chest and strode with widened gait.
He tucked his snout to vaunt his macho symbols;
those budding antlers stood like boney thimbles.

"If any foe would dare to try their luck
they'd feel Sinclair's big thunder-kick and buck!
I'd give'em one of these! (hind legs stabbing)
I'd give'em one of those!" (front legs jabbing)

Sinclair had dropped an unseen enemy
and showed the fallen little empathy.
His triumph's trumpet was a snorting grunt,
while Mama Dawn had frowned at his affront.

The fawn then capered energetically
as Dawn remarked apologetically,
"Oh, please forgive this young and haughty stag!"
His wagging tail, a waving victor's flag.

Though Abel chuckled, also he admired
his fearlessness. It's something he desired,
yet Abel saw the immaturity,
how pride's a shroud for insecurity.

Then breaking character in his charade,
Sinclair asked Abelbee, "Are you afraid?"
An honest moment shared between the two,
where Abel said, "I'm much more scared than you."

"You got that right!" He strutted as he strolled.
The fawn returned to his performing role.
His saunter showing overconfidence
became a prancing dance of deerish dominance.

Poor Mama Dawn could only shake her head:
"It's like he hasn't heard a word I've said.
Stay close, Sinclair!" He marched as bugles played
within imagined victory's parade.

STAY

But then she asked of Abelbee, "My dear,
I wonder—why are you alone out here?
Have you no mama looking after you?"
He said, "My mother's with me, that is true.

"Yet still, this journey I must bear alone."
The deer could sense distress in Abel's tone.
"Oh dear, here's Mama Dawn. Why don't you stay?"
—"I thank you but I really can't delay.

"I'm heading East to Hannahgoode and now
I need to safely skirt the Strait somehow."
—"Well don't head North, that's not a place for bees
because the wasps are all up in those trees.

"Please always keep the Strait on your left side,
for then the seam will be your silent guide.
The path will lead you to a sanctuary,
to Leahlora's garden park and prairie.

"Until you reach it, dear, you shouldn't stop,
and never venture deep in Timber Top."
Just then, the mother's ears became alert
and periscoped. Her body froze inert.

Her head then quickly jerked and turned away
and looked to where she'd left Sinclair in play:
"I'm sorry Abelbee, I have to run.
Sinclair!" She bounded off, "Where are you, son?!"

GIVE UP THEIR WINGS

Young Abel flew ahead with extra care
respecting dangers that the Strait could bear.
But in the clearing, Abel spotted something,
perhaps a predator was crouched and hunting.

All Abel saw was light brown hide like felt
but couldn't tell which varmint wore the pelt.
So, he flew higher than a claw could scratch,
yes, higher than a leap or pounce could snatch.

It wasn't still because it stalked its prey.
Deep in unwaking sleep, the creature lay.
Our Abel saw the famished flies in feast,
consuming all respect of the deceased.

A true disgrace among all flying things
are flies, who should in shame give up their wings.
When flies would vomit, Abel heaved—disgust.
Then one revolting fly blew on a gust.

Defiled in filth, the fly flew over ash
and with the quickness of a lightning flash,
like geysers from the earth, beewolves exploded.
And in one's bite, its horrid head was throated.

The fly's remains were taken under ground,
where the repugnant rest was gobbled down.
He thought, 'Oh, how detestable are these
to feed on flies, the bearers of disease?'

BONES AND FUR

Young Abel looked upon the bones and fur
unable to discern what they once were.
Although he had seen lifeless things before,
into the dark of death, his mind explored.

He thought how things all fight so hard to live,
but everyone's handgrip on life must give.
For death's determined pull is far too great.
Its victory is sure from the starting gate.

When warring worries wage their thoughts no more,
their swords forever fall upon the floor.
A darkness like before our birth is death;
the debt we pay for every given breath.

Then our Creator's life force is returned
for it is merely borrowed, never earned.
And failing flesh to dust repays the ground
to nourish nature's cycle circling round.

But when that hour came for this poor soul,
was any eulogy said from heart or scroll?
Was any somber lamentation sung?
Were any tears, like wells of water, sprung?

With courage, did he face a fierce attack,
or did a coward wound him from the back?
Or did he flutter-fall without protest
just like the autumn leaf to silent rest?

IF

Young Abel mulled. Who'd mouth a mourning moan
if he should stumble-trip out there alone?
If he should fall into that endless sleep?
If Gwen's *come-back-to-me* he failed to keep?

How long would all of Primdale hold out hope,
if Abel's grip did slip from off the rope?
And would his failure be the Queen's last thought,
if in finale's fist the bee was caught?

How would the awful news then reach the bees,
if he ran into ruin in the trees?
He had to shake the image from his head
and reign his fears as Baldwinbee had said.

LEAHLORA

He flew above the seam, South of the Strait,
as thirst and growling hunger could not wait.
At home, with flowered food in vast supply,
our Abel never let a meal go by.

Exhaustion slowed him, yet he onward pressed
until he found the perfect place to rest.
The meadow blazed with colorful decor
a flower-sea collage arrayed the floor.

This sweet bouquet was tangy, savory
and plumed with thick ambrosial potpourri.
This spectrum spectacle of fabled flora
could only be one place... Leahlora.

Her buds, like well, carafed refreshing drink,
and Abel felt cool liquid pour and sink.
It traveled down his barren, dusty drive;
his graveled mouth and throat were desert dry.

He dined on violets, buttercups, and trilliums
and ate from honeysuckles and sweet williams.
He gorged until his swelling sides were sore.
His sated stomach begged him: 'Eat no more!'

Upon a throne of petals, looking courtly,
sat Abel lounged with paunch protruding portly.
The flying bugs that piloted around
were thrumming strings that strummed familiar sounds.

Then Abelbee observed some hummingbirds
with wings that flickered fast, defying words.
They were among the birds who weren't foes.
As do the bees, they feed upon the rose.

BURDEN-BUCKLED

He saw a stream of ants that formed a row.
With deep respect, he watched their steady flow.
The zealous ant—on work his focus stays.
Industrious, he never takes off days.

Their strength and might is in their unity
and sense of duty and community.
Without a single barking ant-commander,
they never have an idling bystander.

One ant was heavy-hauling a big leaf,
while Abel watched in reverent disbelief.
When Abel saw the stress in the ant's face,
he recognized himself in the ant's place.

The ant was balancing a massive load,
with burden-buckled legs, still each step toed,
despite the hardship and despite his strain.
Young Abel grasped that he must do the same.

RESPONSIBILITY

Back home, he had seen many butterflies
but never gave them thought to summarize
that they, upon the wind, just float about
with no apparent purpose to their route.

Their vain and empty lives of aimless ease
are so dissimilar from ants and bees,
whose selfless lives are spent in service-work,
with many obligations none would shirk.

He thought of how simplistic life would be
to waft without responsibility,
to roam and wander where the wind may blow,
to drift with no important place to go.

No rush of urgency is in their flight,
no next-day goals to weigh their minds at night,
no consequential tasks to fill their day.
The lives of butterflies are endless play.

And with this contrast now so clear to see,
he thanked the Lord for making him a bee.

GOLDEN GRACE

It pleased the bee to see abundant life
that seemed at peace without concerning strife.

The hive called Hanni'el housed well-known bees,
such as their Queen named Serafinalee.
High on a birch, called Old Betula, hung
the Hanni'el where heavenly hums were sung.

And nearby, Abel saw a handsome pair
leapfrogging flowers for what they would bear.
Fine pollen dust was rising in the air
just like the golden grace of a lifted prayer.

AN ASSASSIN

As Abel was about to call to them,
he felt a tremor from the flower's stem.
It grew and soon the stalk began to quake,
now rocking back and forth in violent shake.

A gray assassin bug had made a charge.
The bug—macabre, menacing, and large.
Antennae stretched from off its ghastly head.
Its reddened plunger hankered to be fed.

Abel leapt to feet and took to flight
empowered by adrenaline and fright.
Through Leahlora, Abel gunned his wings;
his speed admired by the flying things.

The fuel of fear had burned, so Abel slowed
and he considered to reverse his road,
for Abel knew he'd always have regret
not knowing all the bees he could have met.

And what if Serafina knew the cure?
Then he would have no cave to still endure.
His Queen's commands, though, had been well expressed
and he knew heeding them was for the best.

The Queen said only Vallenbee the Wise
would know the cause for Cimber's dimming eyes.
His desperate Queen would not add to his test
if Serafina could field this request.

Still, Abel wished he hadn't left in haste—
too rare an opportunity to waste.
But now, at least, he easily could find
those Leahlora fields within his mind.

And on our mind is Leahlora too.
So let us copy what the Hanni'el bees do
by sending up sweet thoughts into the air.
Yes, let us close our eyes in silent prayer.

Let's pray for wisdom, so that we can see
that overconfidence and bravery
are very different qualities indeed.
Let's pray for courage; it's a vital need.

Let's pray for strength to work as hard again,
yet it's okay that every now and then
you play and butterfly upon the breeze.
But do not choose to seek a life of ease.

For cynical Sovas take that easy road;
they lack the spine and pick the lighter load.
Please choose to face the challenges of life.
Yes, pray for that. And so shall I. Good night.

CHAPTER 7

To see the illustrations in color, please visit www.TheLegacySaga.com.

The startled Abelbee was spurred to flee,
though he desired to return and see
that paradise. Yet Abel chose instead
to keep his Queen in mind and press ahead.

Within those fragrant fields, the bee will play
in lasting perfumed memories that stay.
But this is not a time for fanciful dreams,
for next he'll fight strong winds and churning streams.

That's one of many challenges ahead.
I hope you'll come along but, with that said,
soon scary scenes will frighten you for certain.
So be forewarned as I draw back the curtain.

I REALLY DID IT!

Dividing Leahlora and Briar Weed
was old Bread Creek that rushed along with speed.
The choppy rapid whites against the blue
were like the sky, yet an inverted view.

With whipping winds, how could the bee proceed
into the pummeling unseen stampede?
He could not wait; the cave had to be found
before the Wood awakens at sundown.

He arrowed into winds above the waves,
but he was stymied back by firm blockades.
He tried again but with the same result.
His speed—no match for turbulent tumult.

Again our Abel shot into the winds
but each attempt had sent him back in spins.
Frustration tears became unstoppable,
to cross the creek appeared impossible.

But Abelbee recalled a common phrase,
one that his mother liked to often raise:
*'A problem will keep giving you a fit
until you change the way you look at it.'*

So, lying on the pebbled beach, he thought
the only way to fly across was not
to go up high where fickle winds were strong
but navigate the caps and surf along.

At shore, his body bobbed to time the waves.
And then he sped, as rushing rapids raised
a curling crest. Arms straight, he rode the swell
and barreled down the drop as if he fell.

His chest was barely off the surface spray,
while sloshing water splashed like kids at play.
He carved a cutback left and flew around
a heavy wave that rolled while crashing down.

When Abel made it to the other side,
he threw a punch into the air and cried,
"I really did it!" At feeling this success,
all Abel's pent-up angst sprang unsuppressed.

As Abel looked upon the roiling stream,
he saw his father as if in a dream.
He crossed that cranky creek some years ago,
when Baldwinbee had fled that Vespa foe.

Remembering what Baldwinbee had said,
young Abel knew close by was Colony Red
and rued that he so foolishly cried out,
arousing rogues that likely roam about.

And so, he left potential scheming spies
because he somehow sensed their watching eyes.

THE MOUTH OF SHADOW BLACK

Abelbee approached a massive summit,
with jagged rocks and sudden slopes that plummet.
Its size left Abelbee without confusion.
He thought: 'It's Shadow Black!'—a clear conclusion

The cave found at its base made Abel sure,
since Ogle noted each distinct contour.
Its mouth was prominent and left agape
like when a shocked surprise has stunned one's face.

As if a raven-colored curtain hung,
a drape of velvet rigged on rocky rung.
What characters are staged behind its shawl?
Who, in the wings, now wait for cue or call?

THE HUNTER

The sun, in fast descent at Abel's back,
would soon forsake the Wood and leave it black.
Behind a boulder, Abel hid away,
eyes rapt upon the yawning cave's archway.

Each moment now could bring a bursting out
of bats with wicked shrieks that ring throughout.

As Abel waited more and as time passed,
suspense became suspicious questions asked:
'Perhaps the bats already left?' he thought.
But Abel had no way to tell or not.

Were he to venture in there prematurely,
then he would be an easy supper surely.
But if, in wait, he spent more time outside,
he'd have to face the darkness with no hive.

Young Abel noticed high a circling hawk,
who then descended nigh from circling stalk
and perched himself upon a reaching root
that stretched out from the cliff face like a chute.

The hawk was watching too with great intent
but out the mountain's muzzle nothing went.
Just then, he heard the sounds of waters rushing
as came a flow of bats like waters gushing.

It seemed the mouth had vomited them out
and spewed the screechers from a forceful spout.
Abelbee clung to a rock like glue
and weathered winds the cauldron's current blew.

Then, from above, the hawk became a dart
that split the steady stream of black apart.
Although the racing river was diverted,
one bat had failed to act when once alerted.

The hawk's left talon pierced its body through,
then its right talon snapped its neck in two.
With kill in hand, the hunter was contented
as skyward the heroic hawk ascended.

THE ONLY WAY OUT

The mouth, again, fell silent—eerie still.
The cloud of bats spread far and sounded shrill.

The words of Oglebee then came to mind:
'Go in when they're away'—the plan outlined.
So, Abel tried his best to remain brave,
a trying test when staring in that cave.

His choices were to go in or go back.
No bee would dare to scale the Shadow Black.
To backtrack now, to find a different way,
would charge a wasteful cost and cause delay.

The Queen was clear that Abel should make haste,
and so, he knew he had no time to waste.
In searching for another manner through,
he might then face a red wasp rendezvous.

From off the tabled sky, the sun was falling
and soon the darkness-dwellers would come calling.
His every path had tolls and wanted skin.
The only sure way out—was to go in.

SOME... ONE

The cave's ferocious mouth was uninviting
with teeth-like juts that seemed designed for biting.
Reluctance pulled, yet he went inching in.
His dagger's point was primed to poke or pin.

The exhalation from this unsavory place
was dank, a putrid gas in Abel's face.
He wished his father could be by his side;
behind that tower, he could safely hide.

Just then a vision flashed in Abel's mind—
he saw the bones and fur and flies that dined.
He thought, 'This awful place could be my doom!
Oh, will this cave be my eternal tomb?'

The ant that hauled the leaf, now towed a tree!
That ugly voice of fear begged him to flee.
But still, the bee pressed on into the throat;
its walls now varnished with a darker coat.

He stopped. From shadows came a ghoulish wail.
What sad tormented soul did darkness veil?
The echoed weeps had caused in Abelbee
a duel between alarm and sympathy.

His fear had boiled water scalding hot,
and Abel could not stop his whistling pot.
The words he spoke had shocked even himself.
With boldness, he demanded, "Show yourself!"

The wounded wailings of the *thing* thus ceased;
its cries told Abel where *it* was at least.
For there's no situation that chills the air
like silence, when you know some *thing* is there. .

In Abel's memory spoke Ryker's voice;
it whispered, *'Fighting is the foolish choice.'*
And Abelbee was stung with prompt regret
that, in the cave, he blindly launched a threat.

Abelbee began a slow retreat—
antennae up, eyes on what he may meet.
When he withdrew and backed up towards the light,
the *thing* approached. And *it* came into sight.

Revealed in luminance, the *thing* appeared,
the very *thing* that Abelbee had feared.
The slender light exposed a gruesome creature,
a single bat with every gruesome feature.

The countenance upon its vile face
did not project dissension but disgrace.
His slouching shoulders sunk with leaden anguish;
long ears lay limp and lifeless as he languished.

Thus, Abel's rolling water that reached a boil,
had cooled and calmed to see the bat in toil.
Cascading light, diffused from fading sun,
exposed not just some *thing*, but some... one.

THE WALL

Though many thoughts were swirling in his mind,
no words could Abel even form or find.
He watched the bat lift up his buried chin;
wet facial fur confirmed where tears had been.

The bat with sorrow: "Will you mock me too?
Instead, show favor please and slash me true."
But Abelbee withdrew his stinger's lance
and stood relaxed with no combative stance.

The bee: "I've no intent to injure you.
I'm only seeking peaceful passage through.
My stinger has been sheathed; I pose no threat.
Can I trust you to share that mindset?"

He sighed with heaviness of heart and said,
"A bat that's full of fear is already dead,
so go ahead and pass; I'm not to fear."
A flash of light then glistened in a tear.

The bat was looking past our Abelbee
and to the light outside in misery.
But Abel knew this grief and recognized
inaction caused by fear. He empathized.

He said, "My fear is an invisible wall;
a structure that's formidable and tall.
I dare not climb, for in my mind I fall
into a pool of shame before them all."

The bat no longer looked beyond the bee;
his eyes were fixed with curiosity.
At once, the bat could see the bee was good
and finally found someone who understood.

The bat then spoke and offered explanation,
"My bat kin leave without a hesitation.
But me? Nae, wee Ajax is froze in fright
and stuck in shameful shadows, fearing light."

When Abel chuckled at the irony,
the bat replied, "Why do you laugh at me?"
Denying, Abel said, "No, that's not true!
My laugh was for myself, no quip at you.

"For you, the cave is safe; to it you cling.
but for this bee, it is a fearful thing.
Into this cave, I timidly embark
with legs that shake because I fear the dark."

The humor registered an agreeing nod,
but then, as if the bat questioned a fraud,
"If it be true and dark is what you fear,
how could it be that you are standing here?"

"That insurmountable wall within my mind,
to which great height and width I had assigned,
became a hiding place I stayed behind.
I felt secure but was, in fact, confined
by an impediment that I designed.
To all that was beyond it, I was blind."

—"But still, into this very cave you've come.
How did you climb the wall and overcome?"

"My friend, to scale your wall is worth the try.
The question isn't *how*; it must be *why*.
For when you sit atop the wall on high,
it is a victor's prize no one can buy.

"The wall is won when you become anew;
yes, what you conquer is the former you."

THROUGH

Then Abel felt the hour's urgency
and hoped he had enough in currency
to garner help: "Would you please be so kind
to give direction so that I can find
the other end of this dark unknown place?
Against that ever-moving time, I race.

"I have to reach the end and find a flower
before the sun is out, within this hour!
Oh, can you please advise?" He asked the bat.
A smirked reply: "I'll do much better than that...

"The cave is long and you have just begun.
No one in here will help you... no one!
My name is Ajax and I promise to you
that on my back, you will be carried through."

When Ajax noticed Abel's leery pause,
he warned the bee of the cavern's jaws and claws:
"The Shadow Black Cave is a dodgy place
with foes more noxious than you'll ever face.

"Within the dark are Scorpions and Spiders,
White Olms and Harvestmen and Shadow Riders.
So, you should take my offer, aye, you should;
for none of them will have a deal as good."

At that, the bat extended out his wing
and Abel thought, 'What an incredible thing!
Oh, wait until I tell my father that
I made it through by riding on a bat!'

FRIENDSHIP

Our Abel, clinging to the bat's fine hair,
was braced against the rapid moving air.
His fear of dark was tempered by a friend;
he felt secure and sure he'd reach the end.

To creep along in darkness to find his way
at minimum would take the bee a day.
But with a bat to navigate and carry
the passage through the cave seemed momentary.

The softened light was reaching in the door,
which meant that there were only minutes more
for Abelbee to find a closing flower—
relief from cold and critters that devour.

The wind of flight had weakened as he slowed
and Ajax said, "This is the end of the road."
So Abelbee replied in a thankful smile,
"I'm grateful you bore me this darkest mile."

But Ajax interrupted, "Nae, nae, nae,
for there is this you need to hear me say:
that you, with care, put me on your back first.
Your words were water for my needed thirst.

"When down, you lifted me at my most meager,
and so, in turn, this bat was willing and eager.
And look! You're through and I'm out of the cave!
Due to your kindness both of us were saved."

"Perhaps that's how a friendship forms and grows,
when both sides feel they are the one who owes.
I feel in debt to you, and you to me.
As interest gains, so does camaraderie."

Then Abel gave the bee-salute and said,
"Be noble." Ajax looked with tilted head
at Abel's unfamiliar phrased reply.
The bee explained, "That's how we say goodbye."

But Ajax said, "It seems it means much more
than a farewell as one walks out the door—
a wise reminder how one is to live.
No finer words in parting could one give."

As Abel looked in Ajax' squinty eyes,
the youthful bee began to recognize
that Dallen's words had been both wise and true.
Appearances deceive your eyes—and you.

Because the kindest deed to come his way
was from a bat who could have made him prey.
The fearsome fangs he once considered vile
were now a fitting frame for a friendly smile.

Both Abelbee and Ajax were afraid,
yet they discovered reasons to be brave.
For Abelbee it was to save his Queen;
and for the bat, to help a friend in need.

They both had learned this lesson in the end—
when you are friendly first, you make a friend.
Perhaps there is a cave that's facing you;
please know accepting help takes courage too.

The sun is quickly sinking in the West.
Still up ahead an even bigger test,
to find the flower before the sunlight fades
and not get lured by good-night serenades.

What happens to our Abel on that night,
brings fear to me to even say or write.
But with a loyal friend, like me and you,
and courage in our hearts, we'll make it through.

CHAPTER 8

To see the illustrations in color, please visit www.TheLegacySaga.com.

Please recollect where we left Abelbee,
who faced a place so dark he couldn't see.
He made it through but now he must make haste
for light is running fast as if it's chased.

He needs to find a closing flower soon
or be exposed beneath the spotlight-moon
to face the horrors prowling in the dark.
Let's hope that Abel doesn't miss his mark.

UPSTAGED

This side of Shadow Black was glorious
and nothing like its name, so notorious.

There was a narrow waterfall that fed
a group of mountain ponds just up ahead,
and wildflowers color-splashed the scene
of freshly watered lush and lavish green.

Their hues were muted under dimming light,
upstaged by evening's wonderment in sight.
Its cotton candy clouds and sherbet sky
sure won attention of each passerby.

The stretching sunset shone an orange-red,
reflecting on the water-glass, it spread.
He flew towards the luring chain of pools,
resembling a necklace strung with jewels.

Oh, how Abel longed to linger there
but he remembered Dallen's words, *'Beware—*
go find the flower before darkness falls.'
Then, searching by a pond, he heard strange calls.

He gazed and heard again the call—a croak.
What moaning monster did the nightfall cloak?
So Abel peered intently into twilight
distinguishing the voices of the night.

SUNDOWN'S SYMPHONY

He had assumed these were Linosa's ponds
that featured golden reeds called Windy Blondes,
whose swaying heads were swung upon the breeze
like they were dancing to the music's keys.

Not all the voices in the night were foul,
not every bay and hoot a harrowed howl,
but he observed there was a melody.
Then, right on cue, was sundown's symphony.

The eve's woodwinds, percussions, strings, and brass
were breathed by breeze through reeds and trees and grass.
The hoppers' strings and bows, a fiddle song
as hidden drummers tapped and played along.
The running brook on rocks, a steady beat.
The orchestra performing off one sheet.

As the Windy Blondes in rhythm swayed
and as Linosa's lullaby was played,
young Abel was entranced by nature's scene.
So much, he could not hear his conscience scream.

Intoxicating pleasures proved too great
and dulled his sense that it was growing late.
The bee was caught, enthralled in mid-air rapture.
The Wood had closed the cage and trapped its capture.

The Wood's unseen ensemble sung from hymnals
as jumping fish then crashed concluding cymbals.
At that, the lights went out; the curtain closed.
The night had come... and Abel was exposed.

A WELL-LAID TRAP

The trance as broken by that froggy croak
as if one in the pit mishit a note.
And yet again, the frog's displeasing key
had wrinkled up the nose of Abelbee.

As Abel panned the scene, another call,
but then his side was struck, which made him fall
upon his back. He landed on a log;
the impact made him grunt just like the frog.

It was a shooting, slimy tongue that struck
but thankfully, the bee did not get stuck.
So Abel rushed to search for where to hide,
for closer now the hacking bullfrog cried.

Within the hollowed log, young Abel hid.
He waited while he faced the open lid.
Inside the trunk was musty, damp and dark
with moldy smells of wet and mossy bark.

In hopped the ugly, clumsy, blubbered beast,
who hoped the bee would be his evening feast.
Our Abel's heart was sunk to see the thing,
too big and bulky for the bee to sting.

Plus, its tongue kept Abel at a distance
and thus, he had no way for skilled resistance.
So, Abel flew as fast as four wings could
right to the other end of the hollow wood.

But waiting there was strung a well-laid trap,
a sticky spider's web no bee could snap.
He strained with all his will to wiggle free,
a wasted try for even the strongest bee.

His wings were useless in the spider's net.
Entangled, Abel's stinger was no threat.
Then, Abel felt the webbing move and jostle;
a spider, noir as night, that grew colossal.

So Abel writhed in twists without success,
becoming more ensnared with every press.
He saw her lifeless victims of the past
still mummified in wound and woven casts.

The spider seeped her hot and wretched breath;
her rancid odor reeked decay and death.
The bee and spider now were face-to-face.
Oh, Abel cursed the day he won that race!

As sharpened pointed pinchers prepped to bite,
her glossy eyes reflected Abel's fright—
those empty endless eyes, a merciless black.
She started wrapping Abel without slack.

Again, he strained and struggled uselessly
because her legs had pinned him ruthlessly.
Her daggers, venom-drenched and salivating,
now dripped for blood she was anticipating.

But right before her mandibles could plunge,
a force had snapped the web—a heavy lunge.
That most persistent frog still sought the bee
and broke the web, which sent him tumbling free.

But Abel could not fly; his wings were tied.
The surface splashed and rippled up the tide.
The mountain's run-off water, freezing cold,
had shocked the bee in a muscle-numbing hold.

But still, he spiraled in contorting twists
for sticky strings to ease their gripping fists.
The surface faded further from his view,
but chilling temperatures ungummed the glue.

He rowed against the strong resisting force.
Each straining stroke had helped reverse his course,
but he would have to row much harder still
because a murky shadow stalked—with skill.

A rainbow trout had thrust and whipped his tail
to turn around and track our Abel's trail.
So, Abel oared his wings with fear and flair.
His lungs were desperate, burning, yearning air.

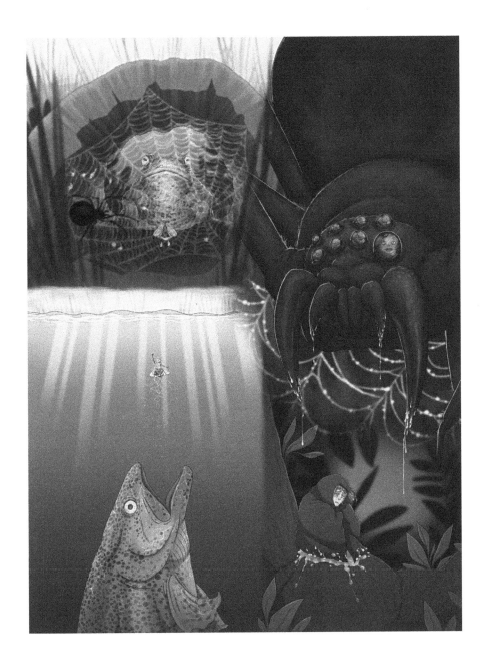

He looked up to the surface, then at the fish.
To reach the top alive, his only wish.
The trout had gained and opened wide its mouth.
As Abelbee broke through, the fish jumped out.

The flopping fish had splashed in violent landing,
but he had missed the bee he was demanding.
Our Abel cannon-shot into a tree.
His gasps were long—his heart in rapid beat.

Since he was shiver-cold and shook by fright,
he plucked a leaf and wrapped himself up tight.

SUPPLICATING EYES

The grim reality had then set in—
that now a night in the Wood awaited him.
And reaching Vallenbee's—impossible now.
His disappointment broke upon his brow.

'I've let down everyone; what have I done?
Oh, why did they send me? I'm not the one!'
he thought, imagining his father's face
with deep humiliation and disgrace.

Would Gwen then ban her tears without return,
denying her sorrowed heart to feel concern?
Would dying Cimber's last command to claim
forbid the bees to ever say his name?

The prize, the thought, the grandiose homecoming,
including all of Primdale hero-humming,
his hopeful legacy, to save his Queen,
now seemed to be a silly bee's daydream.

Perhaps Sova the Great had been *quite right.*
This was a *fool's errand* on this cold night.
And Abel wept a bitter helpless cry
with supplicating eyes to Heaven, "WHY?!"

He prayed for help while huddled in the leaf,
with every part of him in quaking grief.
Like Ajax, he was lost in his despair
and came to grips that he would die right there.

I see your wringing hands of deep concern,
but focus on what this has helped us learn.
We draw from lessons in mistakes he made,
like being lured by Windy Blondes that swayed.

What are the learnings for our application?
Despair, distractions, and procrastination
will tempt and trick and take us off our goal;
be wise enough to not give them control.

CHAPTER 9

To see the illustrations in color, please visit www.TheLegacySaga.com.

We now descend onto a desperate scene.
The villain called the Wood wore gray, not green.
Our helpless hero spent his final breath
in prayerful cries as he awaited death.

But would his prayer impel a caring ear?
By providence, would angels now appear?
Who'll save him from the wicked Wood and how?
Well, let's not wait to see what happens now.

LIGHT

With Abel wrapped inside a leafy sleeve,
the forest came alive in early eve.
The subtle rustle sounds when prowlers creep
could not prevent him slipping into sleep.

Two lights, like angel auras glowing round,
had lit the tree above while drifting down.
But no, these were not holy angels sent,
just fireflies in their nighttime descent.

"What is it Dad?" Implored the youth named Jett.
—"Be careful, son, we'll treat it as a threat."
"But Dad, it's just a leaf bug, is it not?"
His father, Drew, inspected as he thought.

Then Drew determined, "No, it has a spur.
Let's leave it be, for look, we've made it stir.
He's eaten bitter berries and gone mad!"
—"I think it's just the cold that shakes him, Dad."

With wings extended, Jett had moved to see
and shined his light, revealing Abelbee.
"Be wary, son," the father cautioned Jett,
who said, "A honeybee! He's cold and wet!"

With reservation, Drew came close to spy
and looked through a skeptical and squinting eye,
"You may be right, Jetter, but still it's vague.
Move back from there—he may be sick with plague!"

"Please Dad, just let me warm him up a bit,"
said Jett with bulbous bottom brightly lit.
And then, like heat from off a furnace fire,
the bee was warmed and sopping hair was drier.

The father looked upon his caring son
and saw the act of kindness he had done.
This helpless soul the Wood had left for dead
was basking now in warming light instead.

"If only all the world were like my Jetter,
the world in whole would be a whole lot better."
Inspired, Drew began to beacon-blink
the word *'distress'* and called with clicking clink.

The flashing light was seen throughout the trees,
yet no one came, despite the signaled *'please!'*
Then Jett requested, "Oi, what are they, scared?"
But Drew deduced that, sadly, no one cared.

Drew replied, "Don't let this world change you
or dim your light that's shining there so true.
My son, the world's a vandal come to steal.
Protect that light. Don't let them take what's real."

As Drew was speaking, he pointed to his heart.
Again, he fired up the torch to start
his message through the lantern beaming bright.
Into the darkened Wood, he shined his light.

SENT SOMEHOW

The pulsing lamp-alert had caught the eye
of one returning home and passing by.
The stirring silhouette outlined a squirrel.
The light showed brindled fur with flecks of pearl.

He scurried over from another tree
and shared a branch with fireflies and bee.
The squirrel, in study, wiggle-wagged his nose
and he concluded, "Bee in a leaf, I s'pose."

Then Drew's response: "Will you look after him?
All we can do is warm him on a limb.
He needs a home." Then in the leafy cloak,
by light and warmth and words, the bee awoke.

The bee observed, eyes narrowed by the light,
so Jett then dimmed his lamp to burn less bright
and said, "Ah there he is, our honeybee."
Then Abel rubbed his eyes to better see.

The bee addressed the glowing orbs with wings,
"Are you two angels sent with harpist strings?"
—"We ain't no angels, mate, yet sent somehow."
—"C'mon now, Jett, we need to bug off now."

Drew tipped his cap and said, "And all the best."
So, Abelbee saluted off his breast.
The floating pin-lights streamed on towards the ponds,
where mirrored moonlight lit the shadowed fronds.

LUNDY

There Abel sat; the leaf worn like a cape.
His shoulders sunk and slouched, a saddened shape.
The tearful grief that Abel's face expressed
displayed defeat within his conquered chest.

The squirrel cleared his throat to perk the bee,
for in the dark his fur was hard to see.
When Abel looked at him through teary eyes,
the squirrel offered fatherly advice:

"Looky, I don't know what's eatin'ya, son,
but you could face'er or tuck tail'n run.
So, get to livin' or best get on with dyin'
but there ain't not a bit'a use in cryin'."

The stern correction steered him back on course
and for self-pity, Abel felt remorse.
The words he spoke that freed the bat from fear
were now the words to which he must adhere.

Then Abel thought, envisioning his Queen
and what his failure or success would mean.
Revived by honor felt to serve the hive,
it was as if the bee came back alive.

Not wanting to relive it all again,
with no desire to burden his new friend,
young Abelbee decided just to say,
"It's been a very long, incredible day..."

"Lundy's the name," and he put out his paw.
But Abel's hand could only shake one claw.
And Lundy said, "Don't mean to meddle none
but you ain't from around here, are ya, son?"

"I've journeyed far, a long way from the West.
My name is Abelbee. I'm on a quest;
I have a message sent for Vallenbee,
who lives in Hannahgoode by Semper Tree."

"A time'r two, I been to Vallenbee's.
His place out there beyond them silver trees.
I'll show the way but it has gotta wait,
cuz we're dern fools to be out here this late."

The bee was quivering with shivers still
as trembling waves were fighting nighttime chill.
"I reckon best that we get you inside.
Tonight you'll stay with us; ta'mar we ride."

Unlike Sova the Great, that owl scoffer,
came a friendly, kind, and helpful offer.
So, Abel asked, "You seek to aid a stranger
despite the daunting distance and the danger?"

"To gather acorns is an honest venture,
but how could I turn down a good adventure?"
In sync, the squirrel winked and clicked his tongue
for Lundy knew an adventure had begun.

HOSPITALITY

Lundy's home was called the Maple Hollow,
which, long ago, had housed a flight of swallows.
Once there, he met a pair of Lundy's kin;
with pleasant warmth, they welcomed Abel in.

Lindy, his lovely martial companion,
did not at first see Abel or abandon
stacking acorns on a wall display.
Her busy fur, a blur of brown and gray.

Abel admired her prudent workmanship;
her proper planning made them well-equipped.
And Lindy's constant work reminded him
of Gwendolee and those of his beekin.

She turned and saw that they had company,
expecting to see her son but not a bee.
Then Lindy's startled countenance gave place
to honest hospitality and grace.

She looked at Abelbee and she inquired,
"Who's this, our guest, the friend that we've acquired?"
And Lundy said, "This bee here's on a quest.
and so, I offer't him a place ta'rest."

"Well, may this quest of yours bring lasting fame.
Do tell, does our young hero have a name?"
—"I'm Abelbee, and thanks for letting me stay.
The Wood at night is even worse than day.

"The unforgiving road I've had to face
has been unbearably long to Vallenbee's Place."
Still cold and wet, he gave the leaf a tug
and Abel crossed his arms to pull it snug.

"Two fireflies had found him shakin' cold
and warmed'em up, but that would never hold.
He's soakin' wet and rain's a comin' soon.
Without no den, he'd die beneath that moon."

Her intuition saw the bee was brave
but he'd become aware of just how grave
his charge and unattainable his goal.
Reality had sorrow-sunk his soul.

She said, "It ain't the kit I thought ya'd find,
but he'll be back, now that it's supper time.
So, tell me more about this quest you're on
and how my Lundy's mixed up in the pawn?"

"Ole Abel here has word for Vallenbee.
And after all that Vallen's done fer'me,
to lend no paw to him would not be squirrelly,
and so ta'mar we plan on leaving early."

She saw delight that gleamed in Lundy's eyes;
his happiness, she would not jeopardize.
And after hearing Vallenbee's name mentioned,
Lundy's involvement was no longer questioned.

She said, "A great adventure, such as this,
is something that my Lundy wouldn't miss,
and if it benefits wise Vallenbee,
I'd be ungrateful then to disagree."

Then Abel said, "Your hospitality
is loving kindness that's not lost on me.
If I return to see my hive once more,
your goodness will be written in beelore."

She smiled at what seemed to be an honor.
"We'll ain't that nice, but I just done what's proper.
So come on in, the storm is whippin' up."
The hollow whistled—wind was picking up.

Then Lindy wrapped her tail around his back
to show she welcomed Abel in her pack.
Her tail became a warm and fluffy guide
as Lindy ushered Abelbee inside.

A BROKEN RULE

Lundy turned and stuck his head outside.
"Oh when that kit gets home, I'll chap his hide!"
Then Lundy turned back in and hung his hat.
"I tol' that boy, a hunnered times at that!"

Then Lindy, still in usher of their guest,
gave Lundy her response through smiled jest,
"Reminds me of a kit I used to know,
who'd never keep a curfew, long ago."

Just then, a younger squirrel scurried in.
An acorn cluster filled his mouth—his win.
This squirrel, Landry, was their youngest son,
of several litters their last remaining one.

And Lundy scolded, "Kit, this ain't no game.
You know the rules but break'em all the same.
I had to go out lookin'fer'ya, son.
A broken rule endangers everyone!"

THE UNFAMILIAR THING

As Landry took the words his father dealt,
the truth and weight of them were heard and felt.
He went to add his cluster to the wall
but saw the bee. In fright, he stood up tall.

Then Landry angled back in fear's resistance
because from bees, he tried to keep his distance.
Like many do, he feared the barb and sting,
assuming bad the unfamiliar thing.

Once Lundy could explain who Abel was,
then Landry better understood their buzz.
And Landry made connections in his mind
that he had much in common with beekind.

Their ever working, planning and preparing,
indeed were virtues both of them were sharing.
Apparent differences had disappeared;
what once was feared became a thing revered.

He placed his acorn cluster on the floor
and, in an act remembered in beelore,
he nose-nudged the cluster to Abel's feet,
not knowing nuts were food that bees can't eat.

WHAT COULD HAVE BEEN

Before too long, a clap of thunder broke
and rain engulfed the Wood like spreading smoke.
As Abel gazed out from inside the den,
he shudder-quaked to think what could have been.

And Abelbee remembered Ogle's line
about how good and bad and the divine
were forces he had seen throughout his days.
'Did the divine send fireflies my way?'

And Abel reasoned, even if it's true,
the tender mercy shown by Jett and Drew
was from their own compassionate concern.
So, sent or not, they chose their bulbs to burn.

And Lundy, searching for his tardy son,
responded by his will to help someone.
Yet, if these three had never crossed his path,
then Abel would have met the villain's wrath.

The Wood, the night, and now the driving rain
would have abruptly ended his campaign.
He looked at Landry and he saw his friend
was also sobered by what could have been.

The leaf, still draped, was tossed out to the rain;
he watched it fall—no hope did it contain.
With gratitude he looked inside the home
and acorns turned to amber honeycombs.

The hour then grew late and they grew tired,
and one-by-one the sleepy squirrels retired.
The drizzling drops were like a restful hush,
a calm consistent rock, his mother's 'Shhh'.

The bee then pillowed warm in Lindy's tail.
His eyelids fluttered, closed, and without fail,
he drifted off to sleep, safe for the night,
more hopeful now that he would be alright.

And now it's time for us to do the same.
Yes, off to sleep and I'll blow out the flame.
The fireflies will keep you warm tonight,
and just like them, please choose to shine your light.

Sometimes in life a Lundy comes along
to help you right your course when it is wrong
and welcomes you inside out from the cold.
With loving kindness, true friends share the load.

But still, a long demanding road awaits.
'Ta'mar' we'll journey far to Vallenbee's Place.
You'll need your rest, so I'll be on my way.
Tomorrow is the most important day.

CHAPTER 10

To see the illustrations in color, please visit www.TheLegacySaga.com.

The day awoke in the expected way,
a tranquil morning without wind or sway,
but its beginning calm, a false forecast
because the way it ends, a sharp contrast.

One never knows quite what the day will bring;
a single moment can change everything.
Some mornings make for pastel painted days,
yet others, heavy clouds with charcoaled grays.

Will Abel reach his goal to Vallenbee's Place?
And will the Queen receive her healing grace?
Prepare your hearts for what is yet in store—
a day that lives in legend and beelore.

JUS'FER US

With generosity, the day began,
the finger beams of light—an open hand.
A new day gives us reason to rejoice
as shades of gray are given life and voice.

The birds, in morning song, wind-chimed and tinned,
awakening the sleepy ones within
the Wood, who left their warm and cozy beds,
and from their doors and dens, poked out their heads.

As light chased prowlers back to shadowed places,
the grateful animals with lifted faces
were dazzled at the sun in its ascent
and wowed by colors not invented yet.

The bee and squirrel watched with admiration.
And Abel thought, 'A vast imagination
must make these marvels, each distinct and new.
Gratuitous beauty proves His love is true.'

The bee acknowledged, 'There's a genius mind
with work so pure no signet need be signed,
because whom else can make from canvas clouds
a magnum opus, daily, for the crowds?'

On haunches, Lundy stood in silent splendor
with thanks for such a stunning prize and Sender:
"I don't know why He goes to so much fuss.
But don't it seem He done it jus'fer us?

"Each mornin' comes with its unique surprises.
I pity them that slumber through sunrises."
Their path was lit; they started on their way.
No time to wait on this important day.

DAYDREAM

They took the Silverleaf Trail, as it is known—
lined Maples like a seam of silver sewn.
Their leaf-lobes glisten-glint in summer winds
but fall like orange stars when autumn thins.

To Abel, Lundy's pace was slow indeed
but clear directions made amends for speed,
so Abel followed Lundy's bounding run.
His quiet feet, a rappity-tappity drum.
Imprints were left upon the earthen floor,
still saturated-soft from eve's downpour.

Young Abel's mind was free now like the breeze.
Plus, with the mix of silver streaking trees,
along with Lundy's swaying tail and fur,
all things became a most relaxing blur.

His thoughts then drifted back to Primdale Hive.
He prayed that his dear Queen was still alive.
Then Abelbee imagined Baldwinbee
welcoming home his son in victory.

He visualized his mother's happy face
that doted on the bee none could replace.
And Abel's wise advisors beamed with pride,
who, with the parts they played, were satisfied.

Then Abel dreamt about the grand ovation—
the Hero's Hum, the gushing adoration.
And standing in the crowd his dearest friend,
sweet Goldie, spouting sayings that commend.

ALMOST

But suddenly his daydream was cut off
as Lundy slowed, then stopped, and wheezed a cough:
"S'been a while since I high-tailed like that.
So, lemme rest." And in the shade he sat.

Then Abel saw a stump that, like a well,
collected water from the rain that fell.
He found a fallen leaf and made a cup
and scooped some water—Lundy lapped it up.

"That's mighty kind," and Lundy drank a drink.
Then Abel felt his stomach pang and shrink;
his Leahlora feast was long ago.
He eyed some stalks of wild indigo.

With a ferocious appetite, he fed
upon the flower's dewy scrumptious spread.
And Abel's stripes returned to bold and bright.
He buzzed from bud-to-bud in bee's delight.

As Lundy stood, he wiped his mustache dry
and looked around with a keen and searching eye.
He said, "Hey Abel, see that yonder tree?
That's Vallenbee's Place." With pointed paw: "Ya see?"

The mark, unreachable in Abel's mind,
a fictional place that he would never find,
was right before his unbelieving gaze.
He rubbed his eyes to wipe his doubting haze.

He left his meal and said, "We're almost there!"
—"Almost," the squirrel said, with a far-off stare.
"No belly's filled when supper's almost done;
we gotta dangerous stretch still yet to run."

HALFWAY

He said to Lundy, "I am in your debt.
All expectations you've exceedingly met.
The obligation that you feel you owe
has been ten-times fulfilled—you're free to go.

Before it's dark, make your return trip home.
I feel I can now make it there alone."
Then Lundy grimaced with a tilted head
just like we do when foolish things are said.

"There is a motto squirrels often say:
'*It's only the squished squirrel who goes halfway.*'
"Son, wager all your stripes right where ya are,
I wasn't runnin' just'ta come this far.

So, listen here, 'cuz this applies to you:
the things ya start, ya gotta see'em through."
Young Abelbee admired Lundy's grit
and how the squirrel showed no trace of quit.

HIDDEN WONDERS

The famous Vallenbee's Place was as depicted,
but more a modest place than he predicted.
Two trees were meshed like dancers in a spin
with leafy vines pressed on the bark like skin.

Descriptions Sova gave to him were true.
Perhaps not *shabby* but not the milieu
that matched his mental sketch of Vallenbee's Place.
And Abel must have worn this on his face.

For Lundy saw the bee was unimpressed
that such a famous place was humbly dressed.
On his hind legs, he stood up straight and tall
to speak with certainty and spoke for all:

"All kinds've ventured from the far beyond
with happy tails to reach that branch you're on.
Some wonders hide themselves in our plain sight,
but they're discover't when the moment's right.

"It's when ya look inside, the treasure's found.
And all is changed, without no single sound.
A common thing becomes the rarest pearl
that has'a value more than all the world."

COULD BE STORIES

Abel looked inside. No one seemed home.
The room was huge and carved out like a dome.
Collected scrolls were stacked against the wall
and Abel wondered, "Has he read them all?"

Some scrolls with bindings stood in tall clay jars;
one wore the label written, 'My Memoirs'.
Within, what brilliant thoughts must be contained?
By reading them, what knowledge would be gained?

Perhaps brave Vallen vanquished dragonflies,
whose chomping mouths are fashioned to incise.
They will devour anything they catch.
True, even rotting flesh they're known to fetch.

He pictured Vallenbee, a dashing hero,
who fought the many villains down to zero,
as frightened bees, who stood behind his back,
in Vallen's safe protection from attack.

The tested champion of all beekind,
whose could-be stories played in Abel's mind.

NAMES ON PAGES

Then Abel looked around with jaw-of-awe
at all the curiosities he saw:
contraptions bees had never seen before
and things not even mentioned in beelore.

On Vallen's desk, young Abel found a map
with corners pinned by thorns to hold it back.
When down upon the map young Abel peered,
familiar names and placed then appeared.

It was a map of all of Mayfair's Bell,
with diligent detail—to scale as well.
And with accomplishment, the bee retraced
the landmarks leading him to Vallenbee's Place.

He saw the jutting mountains running through
and many vein-like river systems too.
The journey seemed so simple on a map—
just names on pages, nothing more than that.

The Roaring Fork had also caught his eye;
the Sweetbee Common, where hung Pollux Hive
and Abel longed for more in-depth details
of Baldwin's many trials, tests, and tales.

The bottom corner held a clear inscription,
although surprising, there was no encryption.
The name astonished Abelbee to read—
it simply read, *A gift from Oglebee.*

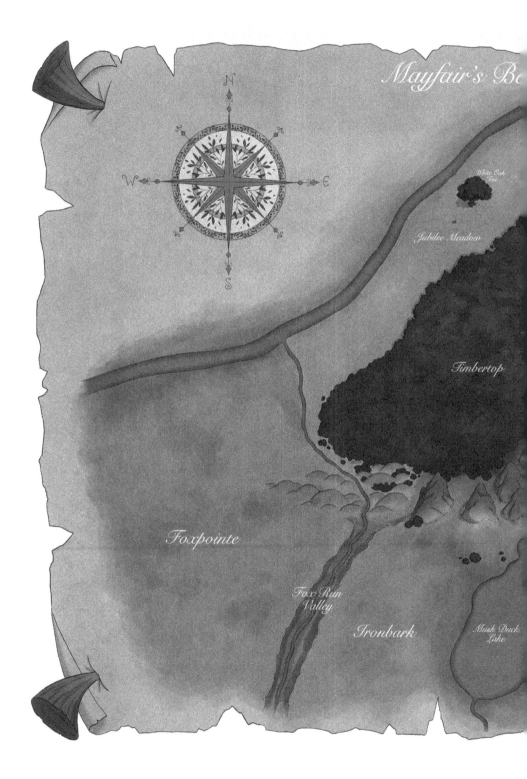

My son, I've noticed that you're prone to boast,
as if our honey-craft was something learned.
And here again, your cup is raised to toast
yourself with praises that you haven't earned.

So listen well and let's look all around:
How can the beavers build without a tool?
Who writes the birds their song and gives them sound
and loads the spider's loom and spindle spool?

Who lullabies the bear to wintry sleep
and then awakens him upon the hour?
Who schools the squirrels on what to leave or keep
and flavors flowers to be sweet or sour?

So do not boast about a given skill,
as if a porcupine who flaunts his quill.

Why boast as if the syrup comes from you?
Do you produce the honey on your own?
Please show to me the nectar that you grew.
See, nothing on this earth does it alone.

Without the soil, seeds cannot take root.
Without the sun and rain, no sprouting seed.
Without the sprout, no flower's nectar loot.
Without the nectar, there's no honeybee.

Were you the one who heated up the sun
to lead the orchestra of bud's rebirth?
Was it your voice that riled rivers to run
and fixed the mix to fertilize the earth?

Was it the soil's choice to house the seed?
Or does the water fuel the land by chance?
And does the sun bring heat for its own need?
A wise Designer's seen at every glance.

My son, please see the foolishness it is
to boast and claim the praise that's rightly His.

Then Abel noticed in less-careful pen
the name of 'Vallenbee' scribed at the end.
Young Abel stole a glimpse of Vallenbee
through this preserved, protected memory.

Then voices from outside drew Abel's ear:
with Lundy's voice, another he could hear.
Though Abel wasn't sure and couldn't see,
he knew it was the voice of Vallenbee.

He hurried to restore the scroll to place
as Abel felt his heart in quickened pace,
which made his hand unsteady, shook by nerves.
He listened on as voices spoke these words:

—"I see more snow upon your mountain, friend."
—"I reckon Father Time will win again."

—"Your visit is a welcomed, nice surprise,
so Lundy, please sir, won't you come inside?"
—"You got another visitor in there..."
—"I do? Well, warn me if it be a bear!"

They laughed. "It ain't no bear or skunk or rat,
but it's another bee, a kit at that.
I help'ta guide'em on his trip and travel."
—"He likely has a riddle to unravel."

"I reckon that he does." The voices stopped,
which made young Abel's stomach seize and drop.
Then suddenly around the entry came
wise Vallenbee in his unrivaled fame.

He strode and stood with height and matchless grace
and wore earned confidence upon his face.
His eyes were wise, astute, and penetrating.
And they implied inquiry—he was waiting.

Young Abel was too overwhelmed to speak
as color fled his face and paled his cheek.
Abel's mouth was like an open drawer,
so Vallen spoke before it hit the floor.

He said, "Perhaps I've entered your abode
and you're the one with introduction owed.
But if this home be mine, then it is true,
I have the right to question: 'Who are you?'."

As Vallen asked, he bent to Abel's eye,
and he awaited Abelbee's reply.
But no words came to Abelbee at all,
so Vallen stood again, upright and tall.

SCROLLS OF LEGEND

"How may I assist you, my beekin?"
Abel thought of where he should begin.
He took a breath, "My name is Abelbee.
My father is a Mason, Baldwinbee."

Vallen interrupted in disbelief.
His interest was insisting its relief:
"There was a Baldwinbee some years ago;
his whereabouts are undetermined though.

"He scaled the Saddle Horn, it's in beelore.
He rode on Sus, the Drake's own Wild Boar.
At least that's how the scrolls of legend read.
Now some believe he lives in Briar Weed.

"Yet others doubt the story this day still
and claim that he was lost at Challenger Hill.
But if you are his son... what piece of news."
On theories, Vallenbee began to muse.

"I am his son, as true as one can tell.
I left him recently alive and well,
but I was unaware he had such fame."
—"Yes, all in Mayfair's Bell has heard his name."

A RARE PUZZLE

Wise Vallen found it rare to have a puzzle
with which to fiddle, one that could befuddle.
He asked, "What brings you out to Hannahgoode?
No, let me guess the answer, if I could..."

The challenge stirred the mind of Vallenbee.
Before he started with an inquiry,
he studied Abel, searched for tells and clues,
for bits of information he could use...

"You've traveled far, of that I clearly see,
there aren't any hives that hang near me.
You're awfully young to be out here alone,
especially, if you are far from home.

"Are those four wings I see? I surely do!
I've only read of bees with more than two!
Then introspectively he said, "Of course.
The Medallion! With scrolls that reinforce..."

Then Vallen rummaged through an opened hutch:
"Where have I put the thing I'd often clutch?"
Young Abel's question paused the busy Vallen.
He asked, "What scrolls? And what is the Medallion?"

The wise one slowly neared and spoke with heft,
"The gold Medallion, fire-forged with deft,
portrays a four-winged bee and so suggests
a four-winged race of bees and this their crest.

"The scrolls are too arcane to fully read;
all secrets of this tongue are not yet freed.
It seems to say a distant land exists.
The scrolls refer to it as Tesseris."

Young Abel whispered the unfamiliar word,
"Tesseris? No name I've ever heard."
—"Well, then I take it that you're not from there.
But if you're not from Tesseris, then where?"

Then Vallen thought aloud as he approached.
Young Abel felt unease as he encroached.
"A son of Baldwinbee?" He thought some more.
"A brave and selfless youth with wings of four...

"Maybe this strange and special visitor
is not the usual solicitor.
And has my time now come? Oh, could it be?
Do you possess a message sent for me?"

"My message is my Queen is growing ill
and giving you this news, her urgent will,
because the cause of it confounds our hive.
Yet, she believes that you'll keep her alive.

"It's only you who'd know the answer sure;
it's only you who could provide the cure."

AN AWAITED MESSAGE

The wise one's gaze then drifted, veered away
as Abelbee's report began to weigh.
Vallen's unmoving eyes were concentrated,
yet after a reflective sigh, he stated:

"The days pass slowly but the years blow by
as if they're clouds that seem still in the sky.
Upon the glance, they're frozen, locked in place,
but they're unstoppable in endless pace.

"With patience, I've awaited word and pray
that message is what brings you here this day."
Tall Vallen grew in stature as he spoke.
"Are you from Primdale Hive on the White Oak?"

He looked at Vallenbee with widened eyes—
unhidden disbelief wore no disguise—
bewildered by this sleight-of-hand or trick.
Somehow, wise Vallen knew which hive to pick.

So, Abel answered, "Yes, how could you tell?
There must be many hives in Mayfair's Bell!"
—"It was in Primdale Hive where I was raised;
I knew your Queen back in those simpler days."

In his retelling, Vallen was affected
like he exposed what he had long protected.

THE QUEEN'S ILLNESS

"I did not know this piece of history—
We really are kinbees then, aren't we?!
Our sickly Queen was certain that you'd know
the very root of what now ails her so."

Her words had raised his cheeks but they returned,
as Vallen's furrowed brow divulged concern.
"I think I know and have the remedy,
for it's the thing that has been ailing me."

The puzzle pieces Vallenbee exchanged
had all been worked and moved and now arranged.
Yet Abel was aware of none of this
and for the youth so much was still amiss.

"Please, Vallenbee, I've flown a lengthy way
just for the words I hope to hear you say.
Do not withhold them, please, what is her cure?
And how can I deliver it to her?"

"What illness plagues our Queen is surely not
a rare infection or contagion caught.
And so, her healing treatment will not be
some cleverly concocted recipe.

"All creation groans and sighs and pleads
with hearts malnourished from a common need.
Although it shouldn't be, the cure is rare.
All could be healed if only it were shared.

"Regarding the specifics of our Queen,
the cure for her lives strongly within me;
my cure resides in safety within her.
See, Abelbee? We are each other's cure."

*The meeting of our heroes face-to-face
at hallowed Hannahgoode in Vallenbee's Place
is now forever kept in our beelore,
as are the stories that are yet in store.*

*We've only just begun, as some would say,
on this one very long important day.
But it's too much to tell in just one night.
So close your drowsy doors and lock them tight.*

*Remember, there's no honor in halfways—
that is the truth, not just some squirrel's phrase.
But do not boast about the things you do;
like Vallenbee's Place, be great yet humble too.*

What wonders may be right in front of you?
What trickery conceals them from your view?
May you awake at dawn with opened eyes
and find the hidden prize no longer hides.

CHAPTER 11

To see the illustrations in color, please visit www.TheLegacySaga.com.

Refresh your memory and let's return
back to the point the story took a turn.
How can the cure reside in Vallenbee?
Let's go to listen in and we shall see.

WE

Now something stirred the wise one's intuition
about their weakened Queen and her condition.
"Please tell me Abel, whom else have you told
that Cimberlee's warm heart is running cold?"

So Abel thought with hand upon his brow.
Had he revealed this private fact somehow?
No lock or latch had sealed her secret case?
Abel felt the heat rise up his face.

How could his lips have been a leaky vessel?
How could his jaw have been a faulty trestle?
And would the hive in whole come crashing down
by his unbridled mouth he'd left unbound?

But Abel answered him with certainty:
"By oath, not even inadvertently,
had Cimberlee's condition been exposed
for I took care in all that I disclosed."

Still, Vallen's heart was ground where worry grew
about potential foes who somehow knew,
and so he said, "It's urgent that we go!"
—"Wait, we?" Confused delight began to show.

"The thought of going back alone had been
like doing the impossible... again!
Though I came here to find the remedy,
I never dreamt you would come back with me!"

"I must go back with you, back to the hive,
for only that will keep the Queen alive.
Please wait outside and I will send you aid;
now I must go, arrangements must be made."

ABLE BEE

Vallen left in a swift and twirling dash,
and Abel went outside as he was asked.
Then straight ahead the bee was eye-to-eye
with Lundy, Abel's eavesdropping ally.

The squirrel said, "He flew towards Semper Tree.
He mus'be goin'ta consult the She."
—"The She?" The bee inquired with no more words,
and Lundy said, "The She's the leader of the birds."

"Like you would say *the Queen*, they say *the She*.
She aims'ta keep the Wood in harmony.
Cielle is also Seer of the Wood,
anointed judge and balancer of good."

Then from above a shadow was swiftly cast,
descending on the branch and very fast.
And just as Abel looked up to the sky,
a sparrow swooped and scooped him on the fly.

As Abel squirmed, the bird secured his clutch.
The sparrow said, "Please sir, don't move so much!
My name is Galvin, sir, and I have come
to chauffeur you to meet with the wise one."

The bee asked, "Were you sent by Vallenbee?"
"No sir, I'm not referring to *he* but She.
Cielle requested company with you."
Toward the redwood, Semper Tree, he flew.

Far taller than the trees within the Wood,
an adult among the children, Semper stood.
Into the heavens, Semper's branches stretched
where Vallen stood in a bald eagle's nest.

The eagle's body blended black and brown;
her feathers shimmered like a sequined gown.
She wore a headdress made of perfect white,
a snowcapped mountain there in Abel's sight.

Some of her feathers lifted in the wind;
the corners of her golden rostrum grinned.
The tree began to sway in the chilling breeze,
and Abel could not hide his knocking knees.

Then Vallen spoke, "Abel, forgive my haste,
but I suspect we haven't time to waste.
This is the Seer, Empress of the Birds,
whose virtues far surpass all spoken words.

"Behold Cielle, the She, who has agreed
to honor the famous Flying Creatures' Creed.
For when the need impacts all in the Wood,
we band together for the common good.

"The journey back is hard for any bee,
yet nothing but a flap for Cielle, the She."
Small Abel looked upon Cielle with awe;
he was a speck next to her meaty claw.

Then Vallen said: "Of Baldwin's family line,
here's Abelbee, who hails from Primdale Hive."
The She bent down in fine gentility;
her eye was twice as big as Abelbee.

That giant yellow eye on him was fixed;
the peering iris moved in subtle flicks.
She shared her thoughts aloud, "A bee... four wings...
a son of Baldwin... now that's interesting!"

Cielle then asked, "Why did your Queen send you?
It's quite an undertaking for one's debut."
He said, "Our hive had held a grand event,
a race, whose single winner would be sent.

"When I was first to cross the finish line,
my Queen then deemed I was the one inclined
to use my speed in reaching Vallenbee...
yet... in my heart, a question gnaws at me."

"Don't keep the wonder in," Cielle implored.
"The questions in our heart must be explored."
So Abel asked, "The race was won with speed
but in the Wood, it hasn't been much need..."

She stopped him there, "You are a four-winged bee
and Cimber knew your family history,
and so she picked the tournament you'd win...
if you were brave enough to enter in.

"It seems she wanted you to play this part;
the race was for your Queen to test your heart.
With brave and steely nerve, you chose this lot
to bear the challenges when most do not.

"The road is littered with talents gone to waste
from those who seemed ordained to join the greats.
Although their skills make them appear elite,
their choices show us that their marrow's weak.

"A hero comes in many shapes and sizes.
Although you wear the best of their disguises,
it is your name that gives it all away.
An able bee is standing here today."

He blushed and thought this was unworthy praise,
so undeserving even of her gaze.
To stand next to Cielle and Vallenbee,
he felt a fraud in such grand company.

Then Abel sighed, expressing great relief
that their return would be both safe and brief.
As sure as his next breath was victory,
his legacy ensured in history.

SUCCESS

As Abelbee imagined his return,
now hailed a hero back from his sojourn,
a different form of fear came into view.
Its voice—familiar—but its face was new.

A vision took him to a sandy place,
an infinite shore that shadows had erased.
The sun was blotted by a full eclipse,
as sand was slung and stung like windy whips.

The fear he'd fail had cast the darkness wide,
with shade that hid a gilded crown inside:
Success—bejeweled in dazzling array,
so beautiful he had to look away.

The voice of fear that often whispered mocks,
the voice that built his wall and laid the blocks,
the voice, the antagonist, the enemy
was now, in summons, calling Abelbee.

Black was the moon against the burning sun
but it began to move. The lid was spun
and light poured out and spilled upon the ground
to bask attention on the victor's crown.

It sparkled bright; the golden garland glinted
with piercing brilliant flashes. Abel squinted.
As light engulfed the crown, he walked to it
despite his certainty it wouldn't fit.

The words *'Be Noble'* in calligraphy
we're etched and dressed in finest filigree.
He dared not raise the crown up off the sand;
the weight, too much for Abel's doubtful hand.

His thoughts gave way—could he live up to this?
And would a quiet life now seem remiss?
What encore would their long applause demand?
Would each adventure have to be more grand?

How could he ever meet what they expect?
They'd see right through the sham when they'd inspect.
How could he ever hold himself with posture
when knowing soon they'd find this sure imposter?

The calling crown then sung in melody
his anthem song, *"Be noble, Abelbee."*
The song was halted when wise Vallen spoke,
"Abelbee!" A poof. The crown was smoke.

A HUNDRED WINGS

With bees upon her back, Cielle took flight.
They soared and climbed to stomach-dropping height.
Then, bursting forth from Semper Tree, in trail,
were scads of birds who Semper's branches veiled.

Each bird took off with calls like horns they'd blow,
her entourage of royal court in tow.
The drone of a hundred wings upon the wind
were like the waters from a dam unpinned.

As Abel saw Cielle's immense procession,
he asked Vallen, "Are they for her protection?"
—"The She needs no protection, that's for sure
for nothing in the Wood can threaten her.

"They come to do the bidding of the She,
in case she needs to reach each distant tree.
They're messengers and when sent on their way,
they crow Cielle's commands, which birds obey.

"They serve as escorts when a council's called,
and carry creatures that are just too small
to quickly cross this wooded vast terrain.
They bring the summoned throughout her wide domain."

A RIVER

Now riding on her back at eagle's height,
our Abel saw a river to the right.
He recognized again the Painter's hand,
who brush-stroked aqua-blue to line the land.

He noticed how a river winds its way:
it never stops for either night or day,
and even when an obstacle impedes,
it shows resolve, refusing to concede.

The water shifts it shape and goes around
or lifts above obstructions on the ground.
It shows determination not to fail,
with fearlessness to carve a whole new trail.

PERSPECTIVE

Abel saw the shape and now could tell
why some had called the Wood the Mayfair's Bell.
The Wood was narrow on its northern side,
but to the south, the Wood was vast and wide.

On high, the Wood began to seem so small,
which taught a changed perspective changes all.
The weighty worries carried in the past
had now amounted to a weightless mass.

For after having won the greatest race,
and after Shadow Black and Vallenbee's Place,
and after being atop of Semper Tree,
and after riding aback Cielle, the She,
the once important things of adolescence
had now become all trifles, obsolescence.

THE REASON

Abel tried to look beyond the Bell
in search for Tesseris, some clue, some tell.
Was he some link within that ancient chain?
What agelong answers could those scrolls contain?

Then Abel noticed Vallen's statued gaze:
a stillness common when the mind replays
the scenes relived on recollections' stage.
And when familiar actors' lines engage.

Abelbee dared not disrupt the play,
suspending those suspenseful scenes halfway,
but many questions flooded Abel's mind—
so many answers Abel longed to find.

Would Vallenbee unlock the prison bars
and free the stories stored in his memoirs?
What rich exploits of such a valiant bee
were cased in the Adventures of Vallenbee?

Would his fine storytelling then appease
the new intrigue around brave Baldwinbee?
The wise one could open wide the door
to galleries of facts found in beelore.

Then Vallenbee began to realize
the weight of Abelbee's exploring eyes.
Wise Vallen plainly read on Abel's face
that many missing parts were not in place...

"I'm sure your wonder runs around in rings
in strained pursuit for reasons for your wings."
To Abel's core down to his smallest cell,
his every atom beckoned Vallen's tell.

"I often thought these wings, a wicked curse,
inheriting an empty pauper's purse.
And many nights were spent in my despair,
wishing away my wings in fervent prayer..."

"... But still, your yearning eyes inquire 'Why?'.
But Abelbee, you can't expect that I
would know the reason you have four not two
because that answer lies inside of you.

"All things upon the earth alive and moving
are trusted with the right to do their choosing.
Thus, I return the question back to you,
with your four wings, what will you choose to do?"

THE PLAYERS

The answer disappointed Abelbee,
who hoped to hear about his destiny,
a predetermined story bound by fate,
but not some future that he must create.

In sensing Abelbee's dissatisfaction,
wise Vallenbee addressed the youth's reaction:
"Though many benefits amount from preaching,
an illustration is what does the teaching:

"The gift to choose becomes its own reward.
For if we're just two rooks upon the board,
then winning has no honor-prized esteem
and no real powers granted king or queen.

"If sweeping moves are not by our own choosing,
then who's the player and the one who's musing?
Who moves the piece that gives the pawn promotion?
Whose mind and strategy directs the motion?

"The gliding knights, and jumping castles too,
move freely on this board as all can do.
We're not controlled by anyone's demand.
We are the players, not a piece in hand."

SOLITUDE

Then Vallenbee went on, "This story now
has stayed within me all these years somehow.
But you deserve to hear it to conclusion
because your valor freed me from seclusion.

"When once I was of age, a mature bee,
I gave my heart to one called Cimberlee.
She was the only heir of royal line,
which only meant that she could not be mine.

"So when I asked her father for her hand,
he gave me news my heart could not withstand.
"The law says that the Queen cannot be wed:
'The crown can only rest on one bee's head.'

"Responsibility to Primdale Hive,
ensuring all were safe and they would thrive,
took precedence above my lovesick heart.
Her father firmly ordered us to part.

"Since he forbade my seeing her again,
my words passed through her brother, my trusted friend.
You know of him I'm sure, he's Rykerbee."
To hear his name filled Abelbee with glee:

"The Queen requested him as my advisor,
because regarding battle, who's the wiser?
He taught me fencing strikes and blocks that guard,
and with this bee salute, he sends regard."

He smiled but went on with his account
and said, "These things are hard to talk about...
but... Ryker said her heart was wholly broken
that she could only weep with nothing spoken.

"I sent him back again to just convey
that I, to save our love, would go away
into the Wood to live there all alone.
And since that time, it is the life I've known.

"When she was told that I would go away,
she said that she would send for me one day.
Yes, when the time would come for stepping down,
the time when she would pass along her crown.

"So solitude was my address till now.
The message in your carry has allowed
my homecoming, back to White Oak Tree
and to reclaim my love, my Cimberlee."

LIFEBLOOD

While Vallen spoke, a thorny question pricked
and Abel asked, "So is she really sick?"
—"Most certainly!" was Vallenbee's reply,
"This is extremely real and she could die."

"Heartache's the illness that affects her so,
the only cure for her is that I go
to show her that it wasn't all in vain.
For both of us this cure will end the pain.

"To many, love is just a trivial thing,
perhaps a brief indulgence, just a fling.
To bees, though, love is not infatuation,
no, not a fleeting feeling, some sensation.

"Love is beekind's lifeblood and our purpose.
It is our true foundation laid in earnest.
True love is loyalty and that's our hallmark;
real love is selflessness for hive and monarch.

"The love between two bees is deepest of all.
In all the Wood, no other hears love's call
with quite the same extent or intensity,
so lovesickness is fatal for a bee.

"And if that doesn't register with you,
you haven't felt it yet but when you do,
you'll understand the truth of her condition
and how essential was this vital mission."

Our heroes are but minutes from Primdale Hive.
Imagine what they'll find as they arrive.
But will it end with happiness or sorrow?
Well, let us save the answer for tomorrow.

As Vallen waited long for Cimberlee
with hope and trust and patience, so must we.

CHAPTER 12

To see the illustrations in color, please visit www.TheLegacySaga.com.

Young Abel was amazed by all he heard
and hung to Vallen's every spoken word.
But when the stirring story came to end,
he started having thoughts of his dear friend.

Then he began to search within his heart
about why Goldie had been set apart.
And Abel yearned to see her face again,
yet now in different ways than for a friend.

Those happy thoughts were instantly deserted
because Cielle, with urgency, alerted
the two about a message on the breeze.
What does Cielle, the She, now tell the bees?

WHISPERS ON THE WIND

Cielle's smooth glide had turned to heavy flaps.
The bees were bounced by muscles on her back.
She craned her neck to speak over her shoulder,
"There's whispers on the wind; the air's grown colder.

"It's paramount that we now make it back
for Primdale Hive is facing an attack!
Please brace yourselves; ensure your hold is tight."
Cielle then rowed upon the wind with might.

The look upon the face of Vallenbee
was when true fear becomes reality.
The wise one had been troubled with concern
that Cimberlee's ill health the wasps would learn.

"A hive-attack will surely mean a war;
I've read of this in annals of beelore.
The vulnerability that plagues the Queen
may have thus hatched a red wasp scheme."

The wise one's face then stuck in busy stillness,
as clear conclusions drawn were made in brilliance,
"Yes, only wasps would use a time like this
to strike, to be drawn out from their abyss."

Our Abel shook his head in disbelief
until his heart was struck with dread and grief.
So, Vallen stated with a brave one's brow:
"Master fear and muster courage now."

Abel clamped his eyes as tightly as they could.
The time endured in deeply darkened Wood,
with perils met and endless trials faced
and every single evil thing that chased;
yes, all the fearsome moments there had been
were unmatched by the fear he felt right then.

The wild stallion Baldwin spoke about,
to Abel seemed a bull with snarled snout.
That brute that pawed the ground was large;
the tiny bee prepared to face its charge.

THE WAR OF BEELORE

Cielle let loose a shrieking battle-cry.
Her entourage then scattered in reply.
In all directions trumpet sounds were heard,
the call that ruffled Mayfair's every bird.

But birds were not the only ones to hear,
it roused an adversary sparking fear
in wasp and bee—the worst foe that they knew.
The dragonflies of Hinder Marsh heard too.

As they approached the noble White Oak Tree,
the hive was drowning in a red wasp sea.
The din of humming heightened evening air,
now deafening the sweetest sounds once there.

Then Vallen turned and said with gravity,
"The time is now! Be noble, Abelbee!"
As red enveloped both the tree and hive,
armed Vallen shouted, "Keep the Queen alive!"

Then off the eagle's back, he shot ahead
in bedlam blurred by yellow, black, and red.
Skilled Vallen struck down two in his first blow,
but war was something Abel didn't know.

Yet, in the swarm he flew with poise to fight,
not knowing if it were his final flight.

FAST AND FAR

The wicked wasps had waged their war in waves.
The big were slow, the small were nimble knaves.
Yet, soon their numbers grew, becoming many
and too fierce for this young bee or any.

Young Abel did what Ryker said to do,
his wings were weapons and so Abel flew
as fast and far as his four wings would go.
His flight had led a cloud of red in tow.

A countless number trailed the fleeing bee,
but Abel's speed the wasps could not foresee.
And as he flew, more wasps began to chase,
a mass that he would never turn and face.

This nemesis was blind by wicked darkness.
Devoid of morals, the wasps in whole were heartless,
which made them seem formidable and strong
but proved their failing fault before too long.

He knew the wasps would never, ever quit.
Their endless rage had made a depthless pit.
Inside it goes the horror they've instilled,
the harm and hurt, but still the pit's unfilled.

Our Abel led the tailing wasps away
with full acceptance of the cost he'd pay.
In dwindling dusk, the bee was heading back,
unthinkably, returning to the black.

UNFINISHED BUSINESS

With fewer wasps, the bee's defense could hold,
as battle blows from bees were dealt and doled.
Strong Baldwin slayed with stout virility;
though muscular, he showed agility.

He powered through the wasps, who formed a wall.
As Baldwin spun, he clubbed and stung them all.
But suddenly, the wall of wasps dispersed
and forward stepped a beast the bees all cursed.

Grim Rory-Vespa had blood-hungry eyes
and opened wide his wings to tout his size.
All bees would turn and fly at Vespa's sight,
but on that day, one chose to stand and fight.

When Rory-Vespa spoke, saliva dripped
from pinching razors that had often ripped
apart the flesh of anything he'd please:
"Are you the greatest one of all the bees?"

"No, there are greater bees who fight today.
I'm Baldwinbee and I won't fly away.
Though I may perish in this coward's raid,
I won't back down because I am afraid.

"I've stood this close to you one time before
and on that day, in my own heart, I swore
that though I spared your worthless life back then,
my mercy would not come to you again."

Red Rory's wings convulsed, a seething shake;
they hissed much like an angered rattlesnake.
The Vespa's ears had never heard a threat,
no, not a taunt—no breath of disrespect.

His wrathful, growling eyes were lava red
from pupils like calderas, magma bled.
"The tariff on your tongue will be your life.
Be sure, you'll find no mercy in my knife!"

Encircling, the wasps had formed a ring
around the bee and mighty red wasp king.
And Rory-Vespa said, "May all bees die!"
To that, bold Baldwinbee made his reply:

"If it's a duel you wish to have with me,
then I accept that it's my destiny.
But be forewarned and careful what you seek
or you will feel the sting this bee can wreak!"

Enraged, then Rory-Vespa charged to pierce;
oh, never was a frenzied charge so fierce.
He roared with anger and with hornet's hate,
but Baldwin's battle-poise was shrewd to wait.

When Rory-Vespa pounced for his kill-blow,
the bee was still—a drawn and ready bow.
And just as Rory-Vespa was to crush,
brave Baldwin spun—a calculated rush.

Exposed was Rory-Vespa's slender waist
and Baldwin's slashing stinger was well-placed.
He swung his double-ended spearlike staff;
as Baldwin spun, he sliced the wasp in half.

At seeing this demoralizing sight,
the wasps, who saw, lost confidence and fight.
Their undefeated leader lying dead
had startle-struck those watching wasps who fled.

The Vespa's son was holding back his madness.
Prince E'dom performed the customary practice.
He kneeled to where his fallen father laid,
removing Rory-Vespa's stinger blade.

E'dom glared at Baldwin in his battle pose
before he joined the other fleeing foes,
and Rory-Vespa lay in death's destruction,
the victim of his own depraved construction.

EXCHANGE

Just then an opportunistic foe arrived,
one loathed by any wasp or bee alive,
those flesh-devouring scavengers most harsh,
the dreadful dragonflies of Hinder Marsh.

The dragonfly battalion rushed and surged,
a timed attack that shocked and scourged
the unsuspecting squads of wasps and bees.
The huge Dragoons had brought them to their knees.

Somehow, a few red wasps had found a way
around the fast Dragoons invading wave.
Their Dragor, Lükalura, was alone.
With pointed scepter, he dispatched his drones.

Their Dragor was a strong unscrupulous savage,
who groomed his army to decimate and ravage.
But with the dragonfly's surprising raid,
they left their liege without protective aid.

Five wasps attacked at once and took him down.
They pinned the Dragor and they cracked his crown.

The five-on-one would down the dragonfly.
Without assistance Lük was sure to die.
While fighting, Rykerbee observed the blitz
where wasps were tearing Lük by feet and wrists.

At witnessing his helpless enemy,
the General expressed true empathy.
The clear injustice of the wasps' attack
had triggered Rykerbee's instinct to act.

In swordsman stealth, he flew without a sound
and grabbed a stinger laying on the ground.
With barb in hand, one wasp he fatal-struck.
His stinger pierced another... but got stuck!

As Ryker tried to pull his stinger free,
the Dragor Lük fought off the other three.
Two occupied the fighting dragonfly,
yet one avoided Lükalura's eye.

The sneaking wasp, with hatred to the brim,
had snuck behind with Ryker's back to him.
Then, deep in Ryker's back, he drove his blade.
The groan was sharp but sputtered, quick to fade.

A fatal wound as any of them knew;
yes, Rykerbee was dealt a sting that's true.
But Lük cut down the heartless wasp attacker
and bent to Ryker to remove the dagger.

As Ryker gasped and grimaced through the pain,
the Dragor spoke, "Your life is not in vain.
I don't know why you traded lives with me
but this exchange has made this savage see
the differences between a wasp and bee,
and only one is my true enemy."

Then Lükalura bellowed out his call—
a long consistent siren heard by all.
It was a message for the dragonflies:
"Turn on the wasps, the bees are now allies!"

Now with Dragoons, the victory was sure,
although for Rykerbee there was no cure.
Then Ryker groaned, "G-get..me to..my Queen."
The Dragor carried him from off the scene.

TIME CEASED TO BE

Inside the hive, faint Ryker raised his hand
to point the way, no words could he command.
He led him to the palace, through the gate.
The moment's urgency, it could not wait.

The many fighting bees were shocked to see
a dragonfly concerned about a bee.
Upon his shoulder, Rykerbee was bent;
the two had found her chambers—in they went.

The dragonfly could hear a fight ongoing
that echoed through the halls. The noise was growing.
Around the corner, Lük had turned to see,
in fever-heated battle, Vallenbee.

In flowing streams from down another hall,
a river red came wasps with swords to maul.
But Vallen fought like in a scripted dance.
He'd pirouette to block, chasse to lance.

Queen Cimber's chamber door was broken in.
At seeing Lük, who slumped her wounded kin,
she showed her sword at this apparent threat,
but Lük laid Ryker down in soft regret.

And then he turned to Vallen—joining in—
the dragonfly and bee, a mighty wind,
together fighting off each rash of red.
The channel's current seemed to never end.

Despite the fighting flurry's disarray
and sounds of pandemonium at play,
a quiet moment passed—time ceased to be
for Ryker, cradle-held by Cimberlee.

In loving arms, he took his final breath;
the selfless warrior had tasted death.

GREATNESS

Then one-by-one the wasps were slain and felled;
the red attack appeared to have been quelled.
So Vallen knelt next to his Cimberlee—
his tears expressing bitter sympathy.

But then, they looked at Lük for explanation.
Why would the Dragor aid those of beenation?
The Dragor spoke, "No bee's a foe of mine.
I see I've lived a life of hate that's blind.

"But when my enemy became my friend,
he brought my blindness to an instant end
by showing me what greatness really is—
a willingness to give all that was his.

"The way I measured greatness was mistaken;
it's what you've given, not by what you've taken.
The air I breathe, a gift from this great bee.
What I give back? To have no hate in me."

SACRIFICE

Then they all looked at Ryker and they knew
heroic actions turned a cold heart true.
The Queen and Vallen understood right then,
his life was sacrificed to ransom them.

Upon her brother, Cimberlee looked down;
no bee was half as loyal to her crown.
Although she tried to keep her composure,
her wound was just too deep an exposure.

Then Cimberlee, still postured on her knees,
with eyes to Heaven lifted up a "PLEASE!"
And Vallen said, beside his fallen friend,
"I wish I had the means to somehow mend."

He closely held the Queen who shook and wept
and then, through tears, she said, "His vow he kept.
But oh, such pain will come from all of this."
She touched his face, "This bee I'll greatly miss.

"We will lament as one, respecting all,
paying homage with our sorrowed call.
For there is no life worth more than another;
each bee, a son, a father, or... a brother."

She paused, while choking back the raw emotion,
so Vallenbee completed Cimber's notion:
"Each gave the same, yes, all they had to give,
thus earning deep respect from those who live."

BE NOBLE, COMRADE

He used his hand to cover Ryker's eyes,
as Vallen summoned words for his good-bye:

"Be noble, comrade. Ry, you lived your creed
and you upheld the code in times of need.
For years-of-years, we'll speak about your part.
Not even death can stop a noble heart."

Then Vallen lifted up his lifeless friend
with gratitude for Ryker's selfless spend.
With the Queen, they passed the palace gate
and saw the consequence from acts of hate.

With head held high, the Queen began to hum
a fitting, pensive family requiem.
With blinks, thin streams of grieving tears would fall,
not just for Rykerbee but for them all.

But then, the humming stopped and so did she.
The Queen asked Vallen, "Where is Abelbee?"

In history, including all beelore,
there had not been such catastrophic war.
This is a tragic way to end the night
but that's the only outcome of a fight.

Poor Rykerbee and all those who were lost,
had paid their hive a grave eternal cost.
But what about our hero, Abelbee,
who lured away the wasps into the trees?

Will he return to war-torn Primdale Hive?
Or maybe, he does not come out alive.
Does Abel leave a martyr's legacy,
in manner of his mentor, Rykerbee?

Those answers and the more are sure to come,
but now it's time for quiet, little one.
Shhh, wipe your tears and trust that he's okay.
Remember, goodness somehow finds a way.

CHAPTER 13

To see the illustrations in color, please visit www.TheLegacySaga.com.

This chronicle proceeds at dawn of day,
where air is steeped in grief and great dismay.
The meadow's filled with many bees in search
for precious loved ones lost within the lurch.

And what about the selfless Abelbee?
A gloried martyr down in history?
You've come this far, so you deserve to know
just how this story ends. So, here we go...

MORN OF MOURNING

The Jubilee where bees would purr and play,
was now a battle-ground where many lay.
The Morn of Mourning it would thus be called
by future generations, when recalled.

His parents were among the searching ones
who looked for fathers, brothers and for sons.
The wails of woe composed the saddest score;
a somber scene where broken hearts were poured.

Sweet Goldenlee was there and sought with hope
that dwindled in the devastating scope,
but Gwen did not allow despondency
or any change in hopeful constancy.

As they explored, their voices would erupt
with "Aaaa—buull—bee!" as hands were funnel-cupped.
Their calls and wishful looks were to the Wood
but nothing came; the trees, in silence, stood.

Against the far horizon, something flew;
a tiny, blackened shape approached and grew.
The rising sun had lit the cloudless sky;
they squinted as a giant bird flew by.

Then Baldwin spoke, yet to himself he said,
"The She." Cielle passed by them overhead.

With outspread wings, she soared toward the Oak.
When landing, it was like the tree awoke.
It shook responding to the weighty bird,
then bees spilled from the hive, commotion heard.

Around Cielle, the bees were grouped as one.
Her feathers brightened by the dawning sun.
They knew this bird of finest reputation,
so they went voiceless with anticipation.

Her splendor had surpassed the legends told;
she shined of grandeur brilliant to behold,
as if Cielle was clad in flawless thread.
The She then bent by lowering her head.

Upon her back and curled like in a ball
was Abel grasping feathers, not to fall.
Her headdress hung like braided macrame,
a weblike pattern laced in fine array.

Abel repelled down braids as cheers rang loud.
Our hero by Cielle was standing proud.

THE HERO'S HUM

Both Gwen and Baldwin, first in disbelief,
embraced and lifted weightless with relief.
And there was no withholding Goldie's tears.
She saw that Abel triumphed over fears.

Then Vallenbee and Cimberlee made way
with debts of thanks they never could repay.
The Queen then raised her arms, "I must beseech
that Abelbee explains. A speech! A speech!"

They saw the true exhaustion in his face
as Abelbee described the red wasp chase.
"A battle was a thing unknown to me,
so Rykerbee instilled one strategy.

"He said *fly fast and far* and so I flew.
Our General, who's shrewd and solid, knew
the wasps would follow, seeking an attack.
The humming cloud was breathing on my back.

"Yes, fifty wasps in chase, if not three-score,
each villain with a quenchless thirst for war.
I heard their throaty cackles, taunts and threats,
a nightmare that I wish I could forget.

"Within the Wood, I darted and I weaved,
and all the while I trusted and believed
that you, my kin, would win this senseless fight.
That with these wasps away, you'd be alright.

"Avoiding them I dipped and looped and turned,
consuming power as my muscles burned.
When both my energy and speed had waned,
the unrelenting wasps in hunt had gained.

"Just as the wasps were closing in on me,
Cielle then swooped me up into a tree.
The She had summoned birds throughout the Wood.
Her words were true, and true, her word was good.

"At her command the Wood had come alive
as countless birds and bats began to dive.
Yes, sparrows, mockers, even wrens galore,
and peckers, martins, thrushes, swifts and more.

"Their piercing echoed calls rang out and soared—
a feeding frenzy never seen before.
Their ambush quickly gathered all they claimed
until not even one red wasp remained."

The crowd gave Abelbee his grand ovation,
their warmth that showed the pride of all beenation.
The Hero's Hum it's called within beelore,
a bee-tradition from the hives of yore.

Our Abel gazed into familiar eyes:
those of his Queen and Vallenbee the wise,
and Oglebee's, whose eyes had seen so much.
But then he felt his mother's gentle touch.

With both her loving hands behind his head,
his mother looked into his face and said,
"Oh, welcome home my precious Honeybee.
My son, thank you for coming back to me."

No words from Baldwinbee, but Abel knew
his father loved him. Nothing was more true.
On Abel's back was Baldwin's heavy hand;
there never was a Hero's Hum so grand.

A TIME LIKE THIS

Once Abelbee recouped with time to rest,
his heart and mind desired one request—
to be with Goldie and give explanation.
His hands were sweaty with anticipation.

His seeing her established it all the more,
that his emotions differed from before.
His every moment doubting safe return
and every dire twist and dreadful turn,
yes, every second spent alone out there
had primed his heart. Now Abel felt prepared
for anything that might now come his way.
But could he voice the hardest thing to say?

The fear his love for her was unrequited,
the fear her fire had not been ignited,
the fear their friendship could now be at stake,
the fear these feelings were a fool's mistake
were equal doubts he felt before the race.

He recognized his fear's most ugly face
and too its voice that spoke outside the cave.
Again, it tried its paralyzing wave.

But for the first time in this whole narration
he did not pause at feeling fear's sensation.
Since words can only ruin a time like this,
he held her hand and she allowed his kiss.

He got what Lundy meant at Vallenbee's
that, though in view, some things we cannot see.
His Goldie was that wonder lost from sight
but Abel saw her now, the moment—right.

Strong Abel was that river through the Wood
that always moved ahead despite what stood.
By never giving up, the bee prevailed
and Abel carved himself a whole new trail.

THE TOP

With Goldie held in Abel's close embrace,
the weight of weary roads to Vallenbee's Place
had lifted off of him. And he was new.
He sat atop the wall and loved the view.

The room then filled. The Queen and Vallenbee
arrived with Baldwin and his Gwendolee.
With faces wide with joy, they joined the pair
within a group embrace, their blessings shared.

Then Vallen asked them, "Would you please allow
Abel and me a private moment now?"
The bees with Goldie, the daughter they adored,
agreed and left the room and closed the door.

When once they were alone, then Vallen said
as weight of sad regret had hung his head,
"I never had a son. And never will.
I'll never know that love or have that thrill.

"But when I dream, I dream a son like you."
Abel said, "These words—too kind and can't be true
for I would kneel to any son of yours.
He'd have the type of greatness that endures."

"Don't let the fear of greatness or success
have any voice or you shall acquiesce
to groping hands that reach to keep you bound.
Keep climbing up the hill and never down.

"Will it be hard? Of course. And you will tire.
But it is then, depleted of desire,
that pressing on, when all the rest would stop,
is how the few may ever reach the top."

Then Abel knew that crown upon the sand
was his to wear, despite its heavy band.

THE MEDALLION

Vallen reached into his buttoned pocket
taking out what seemed a coin or locket.

He spoke before revealing what he held,
"As heat must be intense for gold to meld,
so too the tests and trials that form the bee
into a hero worthy of a legacy.

"And so, with that, I give to you this gift
as a reminder when you feel adrift
and lost. This guiding light will show you this:
the path ahead will lead to Tesseris."

Then Vallen overturned his palm and hand
Revealing the Medallion glossed and grand:
"This fine Medallion's role will come in time;
I sense it better in your hands than mine."

So, Abel took the minted metal piece
and felt its weight and thumbed the raised relief.
A four-winged bee with leaves and marigold
embossed the coin, with stains of ages old.

Then Abel turned it over and tried to read
the strange encryption and what it decreed.
He asked of Vallenbee, "What does it mean?
It is a language I have never seen."

"It is the foreign language of the scrolls.
My understanding still has many holes,
and each new word—its own discovery.
I think it simply translates, 'Brothers Be'."

Abel asked, "Is it the code they keep?"
—"Perhaps. To me, the thought seems incomplete,
but if it is the sentiment in total,
let hives be brothers and forever noble."

"I'll cherish it. I thank you, Vallenbee.
I guess there must be other bees like me..."
—"Those answers lie encoded in the scrolls
as do the bees the Medallion still extols."

BEE'S STING

That evening, bees were grouped at Center Hive
to pay respects to those who gave their lives.
There Vallenbee accompanied the Queen.
Her dress was prim, her eyes restored and keen.

The Queen proceeded to address the bees,
"My eyes have never seen such times as these.
I hope I have the words to comfort you.
Like yours, my heart is still in mourning too.

"The bees who fell protecting Primdale Hive
we will remember, keeping them alive.
That is all any bee could ever ask.
To give them their full due is now our task.

"So speak their names as generations come,
that they might have a never-silenced hum."
Her head then lowered; she began to sing
a lamentation titled, *"This Bee's Sting"*

"As the seasons go,
so do those I know,
gone like Summer's green.

Now that Fall is here
Winter's ever near.
Many seasons seen.

Winter's frozen clock,
slow to tick the tock.
Will there be a Spring?

But when the flowers bloom,
praise with hums to whom
eases this bee's sting."

A silence lingered after singing ended.
A silence reaching all those who attended.

ELLENLEE

Then Cimberlee proceeded to announce:
"The time has come to gratefully renounce
the throne, the crown, my duty to the hive.
I do this willingly that it may thrive.

"The time has come and I have heard the call,
which comes to every Queen, yes each and all.
I gave the hive the best I had in me
but could not match your generosity.

"The greatest gift of all that I've received
was reassurance Primdale Hive believed
that I was qualified for such position,
but now, in ancient, honored Queen's tradition,
I will select your new Queen from the crowd.
I know her father would have been so proud.

"Behold the Queen-to-be, dear Ellenlee!"
(The daughter of the fallen Rykerbee)

The bees' response was bitter-sweetened cheer.
Though Ellenlee was one the bees held dear,
Queen Cimberlee was their beloved one
and they were saddened that her reign was done.

Most honored, Ellen moved up through the crowd.
In awe, they parted and as one they bowed.
A path was made for her to Primdale's Throne,
her queenly glow immediately shone.

They met with an embrace and happy tears.
"I've thought about this for the past few years.
Today to Ellenlee I give the crown.
Will you accept it, please, as I step down?"

Then Ellen, deeply humbled, bowed her head:
"Yes, I accept and Father always said
that since we're kin, this moment could arrive,
and so, he trained my heart to help the hive.

"As you, I will lead Primdale Hive with grace.
Please know it's true, no one could take your place.
With deepest awe, yes, I accept to serve
and give the hive my best, which they deserve."

NOBILITY

"Before the crown officially is passed,
allow one more decree, for its my last:
I ask that Abelbee approach me now."
His eyes were lifted from his crouching bow.

Abelbee approached the regal bees;
in deep respect, he bent upon his knees.
She spoke: "In my last act of sovereignty,
I must reward your true nobility.

"Your bravery and your hive-loyalty
has, in our eyes, made you as royalty.
From this day onward, you will hold the title,
The Guardian. To every hive you're vital.

"Foes dwelling in the Wood and far beyond
will rise again. Beenation must be strong.
Your role will keep alliances intact,
so when the time arrives, all hives will act.

"With this position that I now assign,
your children will possess a royal line.
Perhaps, if they thus prove they're right for it,
upon the Primdale Throne your kin will sit."

A FAMILY AFFAIR

With that, the crown was lifted off her head.
With tears now filling, Cimberlee then said,
"With rights that Primdale has entrusted me,
I introduce to you Queen Ellenlee!"

Their voices lifted with a happy roar.
This passing of the crown befit beelore.

Then Ellenlee, their Queen, addressed the crowd:
"Now that this role is formally endowed,
my first essential business to conduct
is for your Queen to choose and thus induct
a General to lead the Army Swarm,
one like brave Rykerbee of mighty arm.

"There's one who clearly stands above the rest;
he slayed the Vespa when put to the test.

"Seems courage is a family affair...
please, Baldwinbee, come forward and then swear."
So Baldwinbee approached, then bowed and swore
to ready-train the Swarm for any war.

The General Baldwin spoke: "A bee is small.
But size and stature matter not at all.
For what defines the bee is strength within.
Remember this—the truest heart will win!"

Primdale Hive's applause hailed loud and true.
They now looked to rebuild as all bees do.
Then Vallen with his Cimberlee took hands
as they looked forward to their future plans.

Their moment in the sun had now arrived.
One final bow from grateful Primdale Hive.
Outside and waiting to escort them both
was good Cielle, the She, who kept her oath.

They waved with many sad be-nobles said;
a nod of thanks to Abel from Vallen's head.
Aback Cielle, they rode into the trees
where they lived out their days in peaceful ease.

That is the truth about this history,
but who I am is still a mystery.
So far, I've taken care to hide it well.
Be patient. Soon enough I plan to tell.

Or maybe, if I give you time to guess,
there'd be no need for me to thus confess.
So I'll give you the night to think it through.
Tomorrow answers will then come to you.

CHAPTER 14

To see the illustrations in color, please visit www.TheLegacySaga.com.

GIFTED HAND

Our Abelbee enjoyed a fruitful life
with his companion and most loyal wife,
and they became revered, a famous pair.
Their names were known to all throughout Mayfair.

Sweet Goldie's gifted hand was blessed indeed,
producing brilliant art with ease and speed.
Her expertise in many forms and means
had garnered the attention of Mayfair's Queens.

Throughout the Wood, the lofty would insist
her jewelry lace their necks and drape their wrists.
A Queen was not a Queen if in her hall
no 'Goldie' canvas hung upon her wall.

In fact, the illustrations you have seen
we're from her brush, commissioned by the Queen.
The sketches of her private dossier
are in the Agora and on display.

DAD

Of many laurels Abelbee possessed,
there was but only one above the rest—
not his four wings and not his name's renown,
not being Guardian to beekind's crown.

Of all his treasures, nothing else came near
to being *Dad*, it's what he held most dear.
Their cherished children counted five in all;
when needed, each answered their hive in call.

Each child and the generation next
adorned four wings, which came with deep respect.

THE NARRATOR

Since Abelbee had earned nobility,
he gave them all great possibility:

The youngest, Livilee, was kind of heart,
unmatched in beauty, adoring nature's art.
At Warrion Hills, now Livi serves their Queen.
Throughout the Fox Run, Livi's kin is seen.

She cared for animals and flew with birds,
and never was a healing hand like hers.
All creatures big and small would travel far
for treatments that she kept in her armoire.

Their fourth of five was Ellisbee the bright,
the one who brought dear Goldie most delight.
Her deep emotion showed when Ellis left
and from that time, her heart forever cleft.

He went to venerate brave Baldwin's name
at Sweetbee Common, north, from where he came.
He told about the life of Baldwinbee
and that is where he met his Ninalee.

Strong Archerbee was third, a handsome son,
who Goldie liked to call her 'daring one'.
He too had ventured deep into the Wood,
as far as Rogue River, Archer stood.

Beyond Three Daughters and through Highline Pass,
yes, over Musk Duck Lake with jumping bass,
right through the heart of Rokewood, Archer flew
to distant Dennison, the last they knew.

Their oldest son was fearless Arekbee,
the General to follow Baldwinbee,
becoming Primdale's noble patriarch.
Ensuring safety, Arek left his mark.

The eldest was a daughter Maddilee.
And I am proud to say that she... is me!

Now I'm the Queen of stately Primdale Hive.
With this, my father's legend stays alive.
I won't let him become a mystery
or lost to time, erased from history.

The courage Abel showed at Primdale's race,
each test within the Wood he had to face,
each inward battle fought, each choice he made,
each step he took, he took them while afraid.

The selflessness he showed during the chase,
the bravery to go for her embrace
are qualities he's taught both you and me—
and that's the legacy of Abelbee.

Be noble!

ENCORE

"Auntie, Auntie, sing us Abel's song.
We aren't tired; that chapter wasn't long."
A mandolin was leaning on the wall.
The words and chords, could Maddi still recall?

She put the book in place within the row
and held the instrument she used to know.
Now standing in the doorway to the room
were Liv and Cecilee with eyes abloom.

They all now felt anticipation's weight
that one could slice and serve upon a plate.
Queen Maddilee then gave the strings a strum.
The melody, her voice began to hum.

She said to them, as sounding strings still rang,
"Abel's Anthem," and this is what she sang:

Are you afraid?
Who wouldn't be
to face a cave
beyond the trees?

I know you're scared
and feeling small
and unprepared,
but so do all.

The secret of the brave
is that they are afraid,
but they go anyway.
They go anyway.

Were you hurt
by what Sova said?
Do words of doubt
play in your head?

The secret of the brave
is that they are afraid,
but they go anyway.
They go anyway.

Along the way,
you're sure to find
a squirrel who'll stay,
a bat that's kind.

The secret of the brave
is that they are afraid,
but they go anyway.
They go anyway.

Are you afraid?
Who wouldn't be?
But you will reach
wise Vallenbee.

You'll save the Queen
and save the day.
An able bee
stands here today!

The secret of the brave
is that they are afraid,
but they go anyway.
They go anyway.

So what will you do
when a forest faces you?
Be Noble, Abelbee!
That's your legacy!

The secret of the brave
is that they are afraid,
but they go anyway.
They go anyway.

She felt her tears cold on her cheek.
No words were spoken, for none could speak.
Queen Maddi stood to leave and tucked them in
and pulled the covers to each child's chin.

One asked the Queen, "And then what happened next?
When will you read to us another text?"
—"Soon. And it is worth the wait," she smiled.
"Soon. But as for now, be noble, child."

ABOUT THE AUTHOR

At the core, Michael Pietrack is a teacher and writer. He holds a Master's in Education from New Mexico State University and a Bachelor's in English Literature from Colorado Mesa University. At CMU, Pietrack also minored in Theatre, performing in several plays, while playing on the baseball team. These life experiences developed skills that created the perfect storm for Pietrack to write literature's first epic fable.

Professionally, Pietrack is a high-performing executive recruiter, annually ranking among the very top globally. He resides in Grand Junction, Colorado, where his wife and he are raising three young daughters (each making cameos in the book).

Though an avid and well-followed blogger in his professional niche, *Legacy* is Pietrack's first work of fiction: "I wanted to write a story for my girls that they would enjoy at all phases of life, one that would teach them life lessons, in the event I wasn't there to do it myself. Abelbee has no superpowers and employs no magic. He becomes a hero based on his character alone. In the end, that is all that any of us have."

Pietrack admits that when he started writing *Legacy*, he did not set out to write a book or even a gift for his children. It was first intended as a gift for his dad, who in the end, encouraged him to share it with the world.

One may wonder, how did a busy business person and father of three find time and inspiration to write such a carefully crafted work like *Legacy*? Pietrack has produced several videos explaining the backstory to how *Legacy* came to be, including behind-the-scenes information about the characters. This, and much more, can be found at TheLegacySaga.com.